Wildflowers
& Grasses
OF VIRGINIA'S COASTAL PLAIN

Wildflowers & Grasses

OF VIRGINIA'S COASTAL PLAIN

Helen Hamilton and Gustavus Hall

Edited by **Louise Menges**

1984

Claytonia virginica

Sponsored by
THE JOHN CLAYTON CHAPTER
of the Virginia Native Plant Society

Wildflowers & Grasses of Virginia's Coastal Plain
Botanical Research Institute of Texas Press, Fort Worth 76107
© 2013 Helen Hamilton and Gustavus Hall
First edition 2013
Printed in Korea

ISBN (Trade Paper, Flex-binding): 978-1-889878-41-6

Production: Louise Menges
Cover Design: Mary Garner-Mitchell
Front cover photograph: *Claytonia virginica* (photo © by Gary P. Fleming)
Back cover photograph: *Chasmanthium latifolium* (photo © by Helen Hamilton)

Wildflowers & Grasses of Virginia's Coastal Plain
By Helen Hamilton and Gustavus Hall

Distribution of copies by:
Botanical Research Institute of Texas Press
1700 University Dr.
Fort Worth, Texas 76107-3400, USA
Telephone: 1 817 332 4441
Fax: 1 817 332 4112
Website: http://www.brit.org/brit-press/
Email: jbrit@brit.org; orders@brit.org

**BRIT
PRESS**

Botanical Miscellany, No. 40
ISSN: 0833-1475
19 July 2013

Table of Contents

Preface

As one of the founding members of the John Clayton Chapter of the Virginia Native Plant Society (VNPS), I have had ample opportunity over the years to observe and be impressed by the number of people in the community-at-large who thirst for the kind of information contained in this volume. This guide to commonly encountered wildflowers and grasses of the Coastal Plain of Virginia by Helen Hamilton and Gustav Hall and its sponsorship by our VNPS chapter are direct responses to that thirst. This effort stems from a desire to share with others the joy of learning to identify the intriguing plants that populate the roadsides and natural habitats of this easternmost province of the Commonwealth, and also of learning the fascinating "secrets" of these plants. I credit my own lifelong interest in identifying plants and learning about their habitats and natural ranges to the inspiration I received from wielding my copy of the Golden Nature Guide to wildflowers as I roamed an overgrown pasture on our small farm while in high school. Thanks to the excellent photographs of Helen Hamilton and other members of the John Clayton Chapter, and the text provided by the authors, this guide has the potential to play a similar, but greatly expanded and locally more applicable, role in the learning experience of present-day students of our flora.

Donna M. E. Ware

Acknowledgments

Noting the absence of a guide to local native plants, we developed this book following a suggestion made at a meeting of the John Clayton Chapter of the Virginia Native Plant Society. We thank the Chapter for suggesting that such a field guide be written and made available to gardeners and plant enthusiasts. The material that forms the basis of the book's contents originated from plant surveys the first author conducted for national parks and wildlife refuges in the Coastal Plain. Dr. Hall, as the second author, ensured the botanical accuracy of the information and reviewed the clarity of the descriptions.

Many friends and colleagues encouraged us in this endeavor. Initially, we sought advice about the feasibility of such a project from Dr. Donna Ware, Emeritus Research Associate Professor of Biology, College of William and Mary, and Curator Emeritus of the College's Herbarium, and from Bland Crowder, Associate Director and Editor for the Flora of Virginia Project and member of the Virginia Natural Heritage Program Staff, as well as a John Clayton Chapter member.

Mary Hyde Berg, a personal friend and charter member of the John Clayton Chapter, strongly encouraged us to proceed with this project and related her experiences with some of the plants. Pat Baldwin, another charter member, reviewed the list of suggested plants and offered his advice as to their inclusion. Claire Sink initially advised us on the format and development of the manuscript.

Chris Lea, Consulting Botanist, former Vegetation Ecologist, U.S. National Park Service, reviewed the grasses and grass-like plants. Dr. Jerre Johnson, Professor Emeritus of Geology, College of William and Mary, edited the material on the Coastal Plain. Dr. Donna Ware checked the photographs; Dr. John Hayden, Professor of Biology at the University of Richmond, reviewed the entire manuscript; and Bland Crowder carefully read the text as copy editor. We thank all of them for their generous, indispensable support of our efforts, for providing the motivation to begin and complete the project, and for time-consuming technical assistance with the text and photographs. We are grateful to graphic designer Mary Garner-Mitchell, who created the book's beautiful cover, which greatly enhances all our work.

The book was partly inspired by and could not have happened without the photographs graciously contributed by members of the Virginia Native Plant Society: Ellis Squires from the Northern Neck Chapter; from the John Clayton Chapter, Teta Kain, Seig Kopinitz, Louise Menges, Kathi Mestayer, Phillip Merritt, and Jan Newton; and Felice Bond from the Historic Rivers Chapter of the Virginia Master Naturalists. Their excellent photographs contribute significantly to the message and impact of the book. We are most grateful to them all.

"Editor" does not begin to describe the work of Louise Menges during the book's preparation. She brought to the project many years of experience designing and illustrating the College of William and Mary Chemistry Department's laboratory manuals and producing that Department's annual alumni newsletter and the newsletters of the John Clayton Chapter. Recently, Louise was responsible for the design and production of a publication sponsored by the Williamsburg Bird Club, *The Birds of Virginia's Colonial Historic Triangle*.

Louise maintained our inventory of photographs and meticulously selected the photos for each page. As the book's editor, she ensured our writing was consistent, clear, and succinct. And most important, Louise designed the page layouts and endured the many changes to the text and photographs as the editing proceeded. The print-ready manuscript was her work alone—we cannot thank her enough for the many hours she has devoted to the project with skill and dedication.

Working with Barney Lipscomb, Press Editor at the Botanical Research Institute of Texas, has been a genuine pleasure. Initially and throughout the production process Barney has guided us with good humor and encouragement.

As with any project of this scope, the result occurred from the efforts of everyone cited above, and those of other friends and colleagues. The authors want to add our personal thanks to all for helping us throughout the writing and production process.

While every effort has been expended to ensure accuracy within the text and photographs, regretfully, the authors must anticipate errors, for which we apologize and are solely responsible.

Wildflowers
& Grasses
OF VIRGINIA'S COASTAL PLAIN

Helen Hamilton

The Virginia Coastal Plain: Fringe of an Estuary, Assateague National Seashore

Introduction

This is essentially a field guide to the herbaceous (non-woody) flowering plants most likely to be seen on walks and along roadways in the Coastal Plain of Virginia and neighboring states. Included are locally important species not usually found in guides of this type, but very prominent in lawns, roadsides, and gardens, often coloring large areas seasonally. Many are weedy and with small flowers.

Homeowners, members of garden clubs, master gardeners, master naturalists, and ecologists will find numerous beautiful plants that are easy to grow and thrive in this area. This book should be of special interest to landscapers, nursery owners, and landscape designers, who can use the text and photographs to help identify desirable species for addition to the home landscape; it will be a reference in the offices of the Cooperative Extension Service for Coastal Plain counties and for managers of public lands.

Sponsored by the John Clayton Chapter of the Virginia Native Plant Society (VNPS), the book was originally conceived to include only those plants native to the Coastal Plain. However, in decades of field work, the authors have observed very conspicuous non-native (introduced) plants displacing natives in many locations. People will want to satisfy their natural curiosity about the identity and character of plants encountered, regardless of the species' origins.

Native Plants in Wildlife Habitats

With growing human populations, natural landscapes are disappearing under industrial sites, agricultural lands, and suburban developments. Perhaps 95% of all land in the lower 48 states has been altered at some time to a greater or lesser extent by our uses. Virginia's population grew 17% from 2000 to 2010. Growth in that decade in York County was 16%, James City County 39%, Newport News 11%, and 12.67% in the Hampton Roads area as a whole.

While birds use available trees and shrubs for cover and nesting sites, they require insect protein to reproduce and feed their young. Research shows that many more insects feed on native plants than on alien (introduced) species, the result of thousands of years of coevolution. Native plants, through their insect visitors, furnish food for desirable bird populations.

Many insects are specialists, laying eggs on familiar native plants that furnish food for their immature stages such as caterpillars. The Monarch butterfly deposits eggs only on plants of the Milkweed Family,

1

while the Spicebush Swallowtail chooses the leaves of Spicebush; a garden without native plants may not support our native butterflies. Sometimes very specific plants and animals could not exist without each other; for example, the Yucca Moth is the only pollinator of the Common Yucca. The female collects pollen in specialized mouthparts and fertilizes the flower's ovary with it. She deposits her eggs in the Yucca flower. The moth's larvae feed on a portion of the seeds, and in a highly specialized system the plant regulates the number of seeds eaten. Hence both host plant and insect continue to reproduce.

A home landscape can be a wildlife habitat of native trees, shrubs, vines, wildflowers, and grasses, providing plants familiar to native insects, birds, and other wildlife. This book will help the homeowner recognize beautiful plants suitable for home gardens while avoiding and removing introduced species that have little benefit to wildlife. However, it is imperative that native plants be obtained from sales at nurseries, native plant societies, or other sources that do not destroy natural populations!

Invasive Plants

Foreign plants that humans have introduced may grow very well, but their flowers or fruits and seeds or foliage may not be useful as food, nest-building material, or shelter to native birds or insects. And without their natural enemies many introduced species grow rapidly, reproducing by runners or extensive seed production and dominating native flora.

For example, Asiatic Stiltgrass is now out of control along roadsides, woods' edges, and in national parks. Introduced probably as packing for porcelain in the early 1900s, the plant has no nutritive value for wildlife and overwhelms landscapes formerly available to native wildflowers, vines, and tree seedlings.

The first task of a field guide is to put correct identifications and other useful information out to the interested public. Including both native and frequently seen introduced plants satisfies a range of interests, and helps people distinguish native plants that could be used in home gardens and welcomed in natural areas from introduced species to be avoided.

The Coastal Plain

The underlying rocks and sediments and, consequently, the soil that supports plants, characterize the three regions in Virginia. Three western provinces making up the Appalachian Mountain region are the Appalachian Plateaus and the Valley and Ridge Provinces, both underlain by sedimentary rocks, and the Blue Ridge Mountains, of igneous and metamorphic rocks. In this mountainous region of Virginia, at elevations of 1,000 to more than 5,000 feet, conditions for plant growth are very different from those found in the eastern part of the state.

Bounded on the west by the Blue Ridge, the Piedmont is the largest physiographic region in Virginia. Gently rolling hills of deeply weathered rock extend eastward to the Fall Zone, a belt characterized by river rapids and falls. The Fall Zone marks the westward limit of tidal waters, and helped determine the location of many industries in colonial times and the location of major cities such as Washington and Richmond. Today Interstate 95 follows the Fall Zone from Richmond past Washington to Baltimore.

Lying east of the Fall Zone, the sediments of the Coastal Plain consist largely of clay, sand, and gravel soils eroded from the mountains, carried eastward by rivers and deposited in ancient estuaries, bays, and oceans. The Coastal Plain includes the barrier islands, narrow strips of sand lying offshore from the mainland, where plants not found inland such as Sea Rocket and American Beachgrass can grow. Estuaries adjacent to the Chesapeake Bay are influenced by tides and support important shellfish and fish nurseries with extensive stands of Big Cordgrass and Saltgrass in the intertidal zone. Adjacent lowlands are covered with Saltmeadow Hay and Switchgrass, providing food and cover for many species of wildlife. Plants that require limy soils are found in the deep ravines that expose ancient deposits of fossil shells.

The plants included here occur in most counties of the Coastal Plain of Virginia, and some may be found throughout the Atlantic and Gulf Coastal Plains from Cape Cod to Mexico. Virginia's Coastal Plain includes all or portions of the counties of Arlington, Fairfax, Prince William, Stafford, Spotsylvania, King George, Caroline, Hanover, Westmoreland, Northumberland, Richmond, Lancaster, Essex, Middlesex, Mathews, Gloucester, Northampton, Accomack, King and Queen, King William, New Kent, James City, York, Charles City, Henrico, Chesterfield, Dinwiddie, Greensville, Prince George, Surry, Sussex, Isle of Wight, and Southampton and the cities of Alexandria, Fredericksburg, Williamsburg, Newport News, Hampton, Poquoson, Virginia Beach, Suffolk, Chesapeake, Portsmouth, Norfolk, Franklin, and Emporia. (See map.) Residents in adjacent parts of North Carolina, Maryland, Delaware, and Washington will also find this book useful, since many of the plant species and the same habitats are found throughout this area.

While many plants are widely dispersed across the state, occurring in all three physiographic regions (Coastal Plain, Piedmont, and Appalachian Mountains) of Virginia, numerous species occur only in Coastal Plain habitats. Some that can survive only in the specialized habitats of the easternmost Coastal Plain are found only in a few southern counties in Virginia, North Carolina, and southward.

Additional information about the plants in this guide can be found in the Further Reading section of the book, which follows the list of references the authors have used throughout. For readers wishing more information about each plant featured within, the *Flora of Virginia* (2012) is the definitive resource for technical botanical information.

How to Use This Guide

The wildflowers, grasses, and grass-like species described herein are frequently encountered along roadsides, in fields, woodlands, forest edges, and streambanks in the Coastal Plain region of Virginia and adjacent areas. They are arranged by flower color (white, yellow, orange, red, pink, blue, violet, green, brown), indicated by a colored rectangle on the upper edge of the page. The grasses and grass-like plants (tan rectangle) are in the last section of the book. Within each color group the plants are arranged alphabetically by family. Photographs on each page show the most prominent feature of each plant, usually the flower, and the accompanying text describes other identifying features.

Scientific names generally follow those of the *Flora of Virginia* (2012), as do blooming period and common names.

Each page features a single species with text and photographs, listed both by common and scientific name, and the designation NATIVE or INTRODUCED, or sometimes, INTRODUCED INVASIVE. With very few exceptions, there is no doubt that a species designated "native" was here prior to being documented by botanists, versus "introduced" to the area in historic times.

NATIVE plants thrive in undisturbed meadows, fields, and woodlands without human intervention. They have evolved over thousands of years in response to local climate and may flourish in drought, heavy rainfalls, and poor soils.

INTRODUCED plants are those native to another region, country, or continent and brought to this area for horticultural or agricultural reasons or accidentally. While some species may have arrived on this continent in pre-Columbian times and become naturalized, many others arrived with the colonists. Horticultural species usually require constant care in the home garden and often are not successful in the Coastal Plain climate, or conversely, become INTRODUCED INVASIVE, seriously degrading native habitats.

For each plant species the text includes: (1) a description of that plant to help the reader recognize it; (2) the preferred habitat and growing conditions; (3) interesting facts in a comments section; and (4) the plant's bloom time. In some cases one or more additional related species, with or without photographs, may be briefly described on a page.

Names. The scientific name consists of two Latin or Latinized words; a generic or genus name followed by the species or specific name, much as our last names are generic and our first names describe us as individuals. The scientific names used conform with current usage and follow the *Flora of Virginia*, with earlier, sometimes more familiar, genus names in parentheses. Common names can be different across regions and states; the most generally used common name in our area is used here. Plants share family characteristics, and both the scientific and common names of the family are provided for each plant.

Description. The text in this section briefly describes the flower, fruit, stem, and leaf of the plant in non-technical language. Botanical terms used are defined in the glossary at the end of the book. Where more than one species is discussed, the most prominent member of the group leads the text, with others mentioned briefly. Usually the most visible species is the native plant, but sometimes it is the introduced species.

Habitat. This section describes the growing conditions of the plant in nature. Many beautiful native wildflowers will grow very well in the home garden if conditions are similar to the plant's native habitat. Distribution information in this section was obtained from the Digital Atlas of the Virginia Flora (www.vaplantatlas.org), which shows the counties in Virginia where the plant has been found. Additionally, the range of the plant throughout the U.S. (the lower 48 states) was obtained from the USDA Plants Database (www.plants.usda.gov) and from References. (See page 261).

Comments. Some common and scientific names have curious origins, and many plants have been used medicinally or otherwise by Native Americans, including those introduced in pre-Columbian times. This section also provides important information about the position of many of these plants in the ecosystem and their value to wildlife.

Bloom Time. The *Flora of Virginia* provided the months when the plant is in flower. Where more than one plant is described, only the bloom time of the leading plant is presented.

About the Virginia Native Plant Society

The Virginia Native Plant Society, founded in 1982 as the Virginia Wild-flower Preservation Society, is an organization of amateurs and professionals who share an interest in Virginia's native plants and habitats and a concern for their protection. Throughout the commonwealth of Virginia, the Society and its chapters seek to further the appreciation and conservation of this heritage. Its programs emphasize public education, protection of endangered species, habitat preservation, and encouragement of appropriate landscape use of native plants.

The VNPS is a statewide organization with approximately 1,600 members, supported primarily by dues and donations. Membership is open to anyone, amateur or professional. The Society's work and activities are carried out by volunteers. To further its goals, the VNPS cooperates in statewide and chapter programs with government agencies, developers, and other groups with common interests. Incorporated in Virginia as a not-for-profit, publicly supported organization, it is tax-exempt under the U.S. Internal Revenue Code. Additional information may be found on the VNPS website (www.vnps.org).

The John Clayton Chapter

Of the 13 chapters of the VNPS, the John Clayton Chapter is the third largest, serving the cities of Williamsburg, Hampton, Newport News, and Poquoson, as well as the counties of Gloucester, Mathews, Middlesex, James City, and York. The Chapter is named in honor of Colonial-era botanist John Clayton (1694–1773).

Activities include bimonthly meetings with speakers on plant-related topics, an annual plant sale, plant walks, educational programs, and exhibits. Members of the Chapter assist with plant surveys and conduct plant rescues and relocations. Each year, the Chapter's fund-raising efforts allow several elementary and middle school students to attend Nature Camp, a co-ed summer camp specializing in natural history and environmental science education. The Chapter's website is at www.claytonvnps.org.

The annual plant sale of the John Clayton Chapter supplies many species of native plants to local residents. At the April 2012 native plant sale, there were 1,500 to 1,800 herbs, grasses, ferns, vines, trees, and shrub specimens available for purchase at reasonable prices. The plants were grown by members of the Chapter who were at the sale to advise about plant selection and answer questions. An estimated 500 plant enthusiasts attended the event, the majority of them repeat customers.

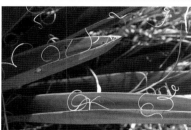

Common Yucca NATIVE

Yucca filamentosa   AGAVACEAE Agave Family

Description. Distinctive, with leathery evergreen leaves in a dense rosette, this plant looks like its desert relatives. On edges of the stiff, sharply pointed leaves are fraying, twisted whitish threads, which are not usually found on other species of *Yucca*. During the growing season each plant will produce a spreading cluster of drooping cream-colored flowers on a 6-foot smooth stalk, followed by oblong dry capsules.

Habitat. Native to the eastern and central U.S. and nearly every county in Virginia, this is a plant of dry, sandy soils and sand dunes. While tolerant of salt spray, it does not do well on poorly drained or wet sites and will not bloom in full shade. After flowering, the fruiting stalk becomes unsightly, persisting for 2 to 3 years unless pruned away. Underground, the long thick stems are very difficult to remove and serve as a method of propagation; many miniature plants will generate from broken root segments.

Comments. Native Americans used the strong fibers stripped from the leaves for baskets, fishing lines, and clothing. Immature Yucca fruit can be cooked and eaten after the seeds are removed. Yuccas depend on the Yucca Moth as their agent of pollination, and conversely, the moth's larvae depend on Yuccas for food.

Blooms April–June.

Jan Newton

Common Arrowhead

Sagittaria latifolia   ALISMATACEAE Water Plantain Family

Description. Growing more than 3 feet tall, this perennial has large fleshy leaves mostly shaped like arrowheads and highly variable in size. Both the leaves and flowering stalks are 2 feet long and contain a milky sap. The flowers are in whorls with 3 white petals, the upper whorls with numerous yellow stamens. The leaves of Bulltongue Arrowhead *(S. lancifolia* var. *media)* reflect the name, as they are broadly lance-shaped, without the projecting pointed lobes at the base.

Habitat. Common Arrowhead is abundant in marshes, ponds, and streams across Virginia, ranging from Nova Scotia and Quebec to British Columbia and south to tropical America. Bulltongue Arrowhead occurs in Virginia only in the counties of the Coastal Plain, and is found near the coast from Delaware to Florida, Texas, and south.

Comments. The genus name is from Latin *sagitta,* "an arrow," referring to the leaves. The species name *latifolia* means "broad-leaved." Another common name, Duck Potato, refers to the tubers produced on the ends of underground stems that are dug up and eaten by waterfowl. Native Americans roasted or boiled the tubers—several days were required to cook them properly; the "potatoes," deer meat, and maple sugar made a very tasty dish.

Blooms June–October.

10

Common Atamasco-lily   NATIVE

Zephyranthes atamasca   AMARYLLIDACEAE Amaryllis Family

Description. These perennials form small colonies, growing 8 to
15 inches tall in loose clumps. From an underground bulb, several
shiny, grass-like leaves surround the leafless flowering stalk. A single
2- to 4-inch flower, waxy and lily-like, appears at the top. Three white
petals overlap 3 similar sepals (the 6 identical parts are often called
tepals). Turning pink with age, the tepals are united at their base into
a funnel to which the 6 stamens attach.

Habitat. Atamasco-lily grows in wet woods and meadows, bottom-
land forests, and clearings. The plant occurs in the southern Coastal
Plain counties of Virginia and ranges to northern Florida and west to
Mississippi.

Comments. The genus name comes from *zephyros*, "the west wind,"
and *anthos*, "flower." The Greek god Zephyrus was the husband of
Chloris, goddess of flowers. *Atamasca* is derived from a Powhatan word
meaning "stained with red," referring to the flowers, which sometimes
have red splotches at the apex of the tepals. This plant may have been
first noted by Europeans on Jamestown Island, hence its alternate
name, Jamestown Lily. Related to Amaryllis, its leaves and especially its
bulbs have been reported as poisonous.

Blooms March–April.

11

False Garlic

Nothoscordum bivalve   AMARYLLIDACEAE Amaryllis Family

Description. This slender bulbous perennial has ½-inch white flowers clustered at the top of leafless stems up to 13 inches in height. Each flowering stem is tipped with a pair of membranous bracts from which arises an "umbel" of 5 to 12 long-stalked flowers. The 6 white tepals are often green or purplish along the midrib on the lower side. False Garlic has grass-like basal leaves only, slender and smooth on the margins. The plant blooms in early spring and again in the fall.

Habitat. False Garlic occurs in open woodlands and fields and along roadsides in the southern coastal counties of Virginia and ranges across the southern and central U.S.

Comments. The plant's name is derived from Greek *nothos*, meaning "false," and *scordon*, for "garlic." It is an onion-like plant but without the taste or odor. *Bivalve* may refer to the pair of bracts below the flowers.

Blooms March–May, again September–October.

Left: Phillip Merritt   Right: Ian Newton

Water Hemlock

NATIVE

Cicuta maculata   APIACEAE Carrot Family

Description. Small white flowers in a flat-topped umbrella-shaped cluster are at the top of some of the smooth, stout, purple-streaked stems. Water Hemlock grows 3 to 6 feet tall with feather-compound leaves divided 3 times. They are arranged alternately along the stems and are much larger at the base. Fruits are roundish and flattened, with corky ribs. Oblong tuberous-thickened roots are formed at the base of the plant; the plant spreads by reseeding itself. *This species is so exceptionally poisonous that merely a bite can be fatal!*

Habitat. Water Hemlock prefers full or partial sun and wet to moist conditions and can tolerate temporary standing water. The plant grows throughout Virginia and ranges from Nova Scotia and Quebec to Alaska and south to Florida and California.

Comments. This violently poisonous species is difficult to distinguish from Water Parsnip *(Sium suave),* which has similar flowers, leaves, and habitats. Water Parsnip has a sweet fennel fragrance, the stems are strongly ridged, and the leaves only once-compound. Water Parsnip can be eaten as a cooked vegetable, boiled until tender, but because of its close similarity to Water Hemlock, it is best ignored as a possible food plant.

Blooms May–August.

13

Helen Hamilton

Queen Anne's Lace   INTRODUCED

Daucus carota   APIACEAE Carrot Family

Description. A biennial plant, Queen Anne's Lace has very flat flower clusters forming a lace-like pattern, often with a single tiny deep purple floret in the center. While much of the plant resembles the poisonous and smooth-stemmed Water Hemlock (*Cicuta maculata*, page 13), the stems of Queen Anne's Lace are covered with bristly hairs. The leaves are finely divided 2 or 3 times. When mature, the flower head folds up, trapping the seeds inside until an animal brushes against it and the seeds attach to its fur.

Habitat. Growing in dry fields and waste places, Queen Anne's Lace is a common weed of roadsides. A native of Eurasia, the plant thrives throughout most of North America and in every county in Virginia.

Comments. Also known as Wild Carrot, this species is the wild ancestor of our cultivated carrot. Science has confirmed its medicinal properties; root tea has been traditionally used to prevent and elimi-nate urinary stones and worms. The lacy flower cluster provides the common name, the purplish flower in the center representing a blood droplet that resulted when Queen Anne pricked herself with a needle while she was making lace. Studies suggest the tiny purple flower at-tracts insects by acting as an insect mimic.

Blooms May–September.

14

Helen Hamilton

Dogbane

NATIVE

Apocynum cannabinum   APOCYNACEAE Dogbane Family

Description. Dogbane is a coarse perennial growing 3 to 5 feet tall with strong, erect, purplish stems branching near the top. Long, short-stalked leaves are borne opposite on the stem. White bell-like flowers appear in clusters at the end of branches. Stems and leaves produce milky sap when broken.

Habitat. Growing in dry to medium-wet, well-drained soils, Dogbane can be found in open fields and meadows and along creek beds, irrigation ditches and fence lines in cultivated fields. This plant is found in all counties of Virginia and throughout the U.S. and Canada.

Comments. Dogbane is a larval host and nectar source for the Monarch butterfly. The roots were commonly harvested in the 19th and early 20th centuries for a variety of folk and other medical purposes. The common name Dogbane refers to the plant's toxic nature, which has been described as poisonous to dogs. *Apocynum* means "away dog!" and *cannabinum* means "like hemp," in reference to the strong cordage that was made by weaving together the stem's long fibers; an alternate common name is Indian Hemp. Dogbane fibers have been found in archeological sites thousands of years old. *All parts of the plant are highly toxic.*

Blooms May–July.

Swamp Water Pennywort

Marsh Water Pennywort

Helen Hamilton

Swamp Water Pennywort

NATIVE

Hydrocotyle ranunculoides

ARALIACEAE Ginseng Family

Description. The leaves of Swamp Water Pennywort are often seen floating on the water's surface, attached to stems that root at the nodes. With 5 or 6 lobes, the leaves resemble those of buttercups, hence the species name *ranunculoides,* meaning "like *Ranunculus*." The petiole attaches at the bottom of a deep cleft almost at the middle of the blade. Small white or greenish flowers appear in an umbel at the end of a short stalk. Two related species are common on the Coastal Plain, both with the petioles attaching at the center of the circular, sometimes lobed, but not cleft, leaves: Marsh Water Pennywort (*H. umbellata,* right) has one umbel of 10 or more flowers; in Whorled Marsh Pennywort (*H. verticillata*) several clusters of 7 or fewer flowers are in whorls along the flowering stem.

Habitat. These plants are common in swamps, marshes, ditches, and wet soils from New England south to Florida and Texas, the western U.S., and tropical America. Swamp Water Pennywort is widespread across Virginia.

Comments. The genus name *Hydrocotyle* is derived from Greek *hydro,* "water," and *cotyle,* "a flat cup," referring to the somewhat cup-shaped leaves of some species.

Blooms April–July.

Helen Hamilton

Common Yarrow

NATIVE

Achillea millefolium   ASTERACEAE Aster Family

Description. The small, whitish flowers of Common Yarrow grow in flat-topped clusters at the top of a gray-green, usually hairy, stem. Six-inch-long leaves are very finely cut and aromatic. Each flower head is ¼ inch across with 4 to 6 "petals" (ray flowers) surrounding the tiny central disk flowers. This disk and ray pattern is characteristic of many members of the Aster Family. Spreading by seeds and rhizomes, the plant's lacy leaves form groundcover, and the matted roots control soil erosion.

Habitat. Growing in various habitats but especially in disturbed sites throughout the northeastern U.S. and adjacent Canada, Common Yarrow is found in all counties in Virginia. A highly variable plant, Yarrow has been treated both as a single species with varieties and as multiple distinct species. In North America, *A. millefolium* is a complex of both native and introduced plants and their hybrids.

Comments. With more than 100 biologically active compounds, Common Yarrow has been used by native cultures for centuries to treat various disorders. Native Americans used the crushed plant to heal wounds, and it was applied to battle wounds in the American Civil War. The genus name honors Achilles, who cured the wounds of his warriors with Yarrow.

Blooms April–November.

Phillip Merritt

Plantain-leaved Pussytoes   NATIVE

Antennaria plantaginifolia   ASTERACEAE Aster Family

Description. The bristly gray-white flower heads of Plantain-leaved Pussytoes resemble the pads or toes of a cat's paw. Male and female heads are borne on separate plants. Leaves at the base of the plant grow to 4 inches long; the blades are spoon-shaped with 3 to 5 conspicuous veins and densely hairy underneath. The flowering stem, 6 to 15 inches tall with a few small, narrow, alternate leaves, is covered with numerous white hairs. With similar basal leaves, a related species, Single-head Pussytoes *(A. solitaria),* has only one flower head on a stalk; it is widespread but uncommon in Virginia.

Habitat. This perennial grows in dry soil in woods, thickets, and pastures from Nova Scotia to eastern Montana and south to Georgia and Texas. It is native across most counties in Virginia. With soft, gray foliage, this plant is easy to grow in the home garden in dry, well-drained soil, and can cover rocky areas and open slopes. Reproducing by stolons (stems that form new plants where they touch the soil), Plantain-leaved Pussytoes often forms dense mats, partly due to chemicals that inhibit development of neighboring plants.

Comments. *Antennaria* refers to the resemblance of bristles in the male flowers to the antennae of butterflies.

Blooms March–May.

18

Left: Helen Hamilton   Right: Seig Kopnitz

Horseweed

NATIVE

Conyza canadensis   ASTERACEAE Aster Family

Description. Horseweed grows 1 to 6 feet tall on a stout, usually simple, stem often covered with long white hairs, sometimes glabrous. The very numerous narrow leaves are crowded on the stem. Near the top, flowering branches bear numerous small heads, each with a yellow disk and tiny whitish rays. Resembling the larger flowers of the fleabanes *(Erigeron)*, the horseweeds were placed in that genus in the past. In early fall the heads of this annual weed bear seeds (achenes) crowned with fine bristles. Heads of Fireweed (*Erechtites hieraciifolius*, page 20*)* are somewhat similar, but the leaves of the latter are larger, more toothy, and well spaced alternately on the stem.

Habitat. Thriving on bare soil, Horseweed grows on roadsides, in old fields and on dry or moist disturbed ground. A North American native, it has spread to Europe, where it colonizes open disturbed sites. It is found all over North America and in every county in Virginia.

Comments. The common name may refer to the plant's coarseness and robust size compared with related species such as fleabanes. Indians and early settlers used a preparation of its leaves to treat dysentery and sore throat. Deer usually avoid this plant because the foliage is bitter.

Blooms July–November.

19

Left: Phillip Merritt   Right: Helen Hamilton

Fireweed

NATIVE

Erechtites hieraciifolius   ASTERACEAE Aster Family

Description. Unlike many members of the Aster Family, Fireweed has heads that lack the distinctive ray flowers. They are cylindric with a swollen base topped with white disk flowers, becoming conspicuous as they fill with copious masses of fine, soft hairs attached to the young fruits. The oblong leaves are alternate, often with sharp teeth or irregular lobes. Fireweed can grow to more than 6 feet tall with leaves up to 4 inches wide.

Habitat. Fireweed is an annual weed invading various habitats, including dry woods, marshes, ditches, and burned-over areas in every county in Virginia. This plant ranges from Newfoundland to Florida west to Nebraska and Texas, and has been introduced elsewhere.

Comments. While neglected by scientific investigators, Fireweed has been used as an astringent and tonic and for muscular rheumatism and sciatica. *Erechtites* is an ancient name used by Dioscorides; the species name *hieraciifolius* refers to its leaves, which are like those of Hawkweed, genus *Hieracium.* The common name Fireweed is also used for a lovely, showy pink wildflower *(Epilobium angustifolium),* which is native to Virginia only in the mountains but an abundant invader of disturbed areas further north.

Blooms July–November.

Left: Phillip Merritt   Center and right: Helen Hamilton

Annual Fleabane

ASTERACEAE Aster Family

Erigeron annuus

NATIVE

Description. This aster-like flower starts blooming in the spring, unlike the fall-blooming asters. The white rays are smaller than those of asters, are more numerous (40 to 70), and surround a dense yellow disk. Broad stem leaves are toothed, not clasping, and long-spreading white hairs occur along the entire length of the 3- to 4-foot stems. Rough Fleabane *(E. strigosus)* is similar but shorter, and the leaves on the stem are linear, fewer, firm, and usually smooth-edged. Short, appressed hairs occur along the middle and upper portions of the stems of Rough Fleabane. Both of these species are usually annual, rarely biennial.

Habitat. Annual Fleabane grows in fields, on roadsides and waste land, and as a weed on disturbed sites over most of the U.S. and Canada and in every county in Virginia. Preferring full or partial sun, the plant tolerates clay or gravelly soils. It is easy to grow and will reseed itself in disturbed areas.

Comments. Various plants of the Aster Family are supposed to drive away fleas, hence the common name Fleabane. The Catawba used an infusion of the roots as a heart medicine, and the Ojibwa used the plant to treat headaches.

Blooms May–October.

Helen Hamilton

Dog-fennel

Eupatorium capillifolium   ASTERACEAE Aster Family

Description. Dog-fennel is a coarse perennial generally more than 6 feet tall with several erect stems emerging from a woody base. The stems are hairy and reddish, especially late in the season. Numerous very finely divided leaves give the plant a fern-like appearance. Lower leaves are opposite on the stem, the others alternate. The very small, creamy-white flowers are wind-pollinated. When crushed the leaves and flowers release an unpleasant odor.

Habitat. This is an aggressive and weedy plant growing in open fields, old fields, and pastures on the Coastal Plain from New Jersey to Florida, Texas, and Arkansas. Dog-fennel is an excellent indicator of soil disturbance. The plant spreads both by seeds and rootstocks.

Comments. The species name *capillifolium* is derived from Latin *capill,* meaning "hair," and *foli(um),* meaning "leaf," referring to the narrow segments of the leaves. The common name refers to the fennel-like odor of the plant, which dogs appear to enjoy; livestock usually avoid consuming the plant. Essential oils from Dog-fennel show promise as a natural insecticide against mosquitoes.

Blooms September–November.

Helen Hamilton

Hyssop-leaf Boneset

NATIVE

Eupatorium hyssopifolium   ASTERACEAE   Aster Family

Description. A distinctive fall-blooming member of the Aster Family, this plant is distinguished by extremely narrow leaves, mostly in whorls of 3 or 4, with clusters of smaller leaves growing in the axils. Growing 1 to 3 feet tall, each stem is topped by a flattish cluster of small white tubular disk flowers; there are no ray flowers.

Habitat. Growing in dry sandy fields and open woods in most counties in Virginia, Hyssop-leaf Boneset ranges from Massachusetts to northern Florida west to Louisiana and sometimes inland to Ohio, Kentucky, and Tennessee.

Comments. "Hyssop" is from Greek *hyssopos,* meaning "an aromatic plant." The narrow leaves of a European herb *(Hyssopus officinalis)* are highly aromatic and pungent, and Hyssop-leaf Boneset may have received its name for its similarity to the European herb. Many species of butterflies visit the flowers.

Blooms August–October.

Phillip Merritt

Boneset

NATIVE

Eupatorium perfoliatum   ASTERACEAE Aster Family

Description. Boneset derives its species name from its long, stalkless, lance-shaped leaves, which are paired and fused around the stem. This perennial grows more than 5 feet tall on erect solid stems covered with long spreading hairs. Small fuzzy white florets (flower buds shown in the photo) are clustered at the top of branching stems. Other species of *Eupatorium* found on the Coastal Plain have spreading clusters of white flowers, but their leaves are rounded, sessile, or on short petioles. The genus is confusing because of varietal forms and hybrids.

Habitat. Widespread across Virginia, Boneset grows in marshes, swamps, bogs, wet pastures, and other moist or wet low grounds. The range extends from Nova Scotia and Quebec to northern Florida and west to North Dakota, Nebraska, Oklahoma, and Texas.

Comments. Because the stem appears to be growing through the leaf (perfoliate), early herb doctors wrapped its leaves with bandages around splints, thinking the plant would be useful in setting bones. An alternate explanation of the common name comes from its use in treating break-bone fever or dengue fever. The dried leaves have been used to make a tonic, boneset tea, thought effective in treating colds, coughs, and constipation.

Blooms August–October.

Left: Phillip Merritt   Right: Helen Hamilton

Late-flowering Boneset

Eupatorium serotinum   ASTERACEAE Aster Family

Description. With similar flowers, the bonesets can be distinguished from each other by their leaves. In this species they are lance-shaped and toothed, with 3 prominent veins; each leaf tends to droop downward from a short petiole. White flowers are tubular, without rays, and a long, white, divided style protrudes from each floret, giving the flat-topped flower cluster a fuzzy appearance. Late-flowering Boneset is an erect perennial herb with hairy stems up to 6 feet tall, often forming clumps.

Habitat. This plant is found in brackish and freshwater tidal marshes, upland fields, and waste places. The range is from southern New York to Illinois and south to Florida and Texas. In Virginia, Late-flowering Boneset is native to the Coastal Plain, and is found irregularly in the Piedmont and Mountain regions.

Comments. These plants are called bonesets because they had been used in treating dengue fever, also known as break-bone fever. The genus name comes from Mithridates Eupator, King of Pontus (134–63 B.C.), who supposedly discovered the medicinal virtues of bonesets. Native Americans also used the plants as medicinal aids.

Blooms August–October.

Helen Hamilton

Purple Everlasting NATIVE

Gamochaeta (Gnaphalium) purpurea   ASTERACEAE Aster Family

Description. This plant is a common lawn and garden weed with densely woolly stems to 1½ feet tall. The lowest leaves are broadest above the middle or even spoon-shaped, and rounded at the tip. The obscure tannish-white flower heads, often tinged with purple, are borne in an elongate narrow cluster. Variability in hairiness and the shape of minute flower parts has led recent authors to separate out a half-dozen other species from the original Purple Everlasting. The species generally flowers earlier than the Fragrant Everlasting, *Pseudognaphalium obtusifolium* (page 30).

Habitat. Growing in open, often sandy, habitats such as roadsides and clearings, this annual/biennial is common in the eastern U.S. and nearly every county in Virginia. The plant occurs widely throughout the world as a weed in disturbed areas.

Comments. The genus name derives from Greek *gamo*, "marriage," and *chaeto*, "bristle," the bristles crowning the tiny fruits remaining united in a ring. The soft leaves of a similar British species were used to prevent chafing and, mixed with fat, given to cattle that had lost their cud. The plant is also called Purple Cudweed.

Blooms March–July.

Ox-eye Daisy

Leucanthemum vulgare   ASTERACEAE Aster Family

Description. This showy perennial with rich yellow disk flowers and bright white ray flowers ("petals") forms flower heads 1 to 2 inches wide. Each flowering stem bears a single head and alternate toothed leaves. Spreading by rhizomes, the plant grows to 3 feet tall with few branches.

Habitat. Ox-eye Daisy is very common in fields and meadows, preferring full sun and slightly dry conditions. Native to Eurasia, this weedy plant is now naturalized through most of temperate North America and occurs in every county in Virginia. It grows unmolested by grazing cattle, which prefer other forage.

Comments. The genus name is derived from Greek *leuko*, which means "white." Wild English Daisy *(Bellis perennis)* opens at dawn and closes at dusk, giving the plant its original name, "day's eye." Ox-eye Daisy, a close relative of chamomile, has been brewed to make a calming tea. The leaves may repel fleas. Luther Burbank developed the Shasta Daisy from Eurasian species. Cultivars of *Leucanthemum×superbum* (Shasta Daisy) can closely resemble Ox-eye Daisy in general appearance, with larger flower heads and leaves with few teeth. Other close relatives are the garden chrysanthemums and Pyrethrum Daisy, source of a valuable natural insecticide.

Blooms April–July.

Climbing Hempweed

NATIVE

Mikania scandens   ASTERACEAE Aster Family

Description. Climbing Hempweed is a perennial twining vine with flowers in numerous small 4-flowered heads; the tiny white to pink flowers are tubular. As in many other members of the Aster Family, small 1-seeded fruits (achenes) have a crown of numerous fine bristles. The leaves are opposite, triangular or heart-shaped, and slightly toothed. The plant often forms masses sprawling over other low vegetation.

Habitat. Growing in moist soils, along fence rows, in wet thickets, at pond margins and freshwater marshes, Climbing Hempweed is common throughout the Mid-Atlantic coastal region and ranges from Maine to Florida, Missouri, Texas, and south and is very common in tropical South America. In Virginia the plant is mostly native to the coastal and Piedmont counties. It grows quickly and can become weedy, forming dense mats.

Comments. Named for J.G. Mikan (1743–1814), a professor at the University of Prague. The species name *scandens* means "climbing." Climbing Hempweed is a larval and nectar host for Little Metalmark butterflies.

Blooms July–October.

Helen Hamilton

Wild Quinine

NATIVE

Parthenium integrifolium   ASTERACEAE Aster Family

Description. Somewhat resembling tiny cauliflowers, the small white flower heads are in large, loosely branched flat-headed clusters. Each flower head is less than ½ inch wide, consisting mostly of disk flowers surrounded by 5 minute rays. Basal ovate leaves are on long petioles, the blades 8 to 10 inches long, aromatic, coarsely toothed, and rough. Wild Quinine grows 1 to 4 feet tall.

Habitat. This perennial prefers average, well-drained soil, dry to moist, in full sun. A plant of open woods, meadows, and thickets, Wild Quinine occurs in most counties of Virginia. The range is from Maryland to southeast Minnesota and south to Georgia and Arkansas.

Comments. The genus name comes from Greek *parthenos* for "virgin," an obscure reference to the fact that only the ray flowers are fertile, the disk flowers sterile. The flowering tops were once used for "intermittent fevers" like malaria, hence the name Wild Quinine. The root was used as a diuretic for kidney and bladder problems and gonorrhea. One study suggests that Wild Quinine may stimulate the immune system. It is a common addition to extracts of Purple Coneflower, known as Echinacea, historically and in modern times.

Blooms May–August.

Fragrant Everlasting

NATIVE

Pseudognaphalium (Gnaphalium) obtusifolium

ASTERACEAE Aster Family

Description. This much-branched annual with densely woolly stems and white, fuzzy blossoms grows 2 feet tall and is mildly aromatic when bruised. The numerous alternate leaves are narrow, green above, white-woolly below, and sessile, but not clasping the stem. The flower heads are small and numerous, in clusters aggregated in a broad group. One-seeded fruits (achenes) are crowned with a set of small bristly hairs.

Habitat. Found in pastures, fields, and woodland borders, Fragrant Everlasting is widespread across Virginia and ranges from eastern Canada to Florida and west to Nebraska and Texas.

Comments. The genus is from *gnaphallon*, "lock of wool," an ancient Greek name of some downy plant. Another name, Feather-weed, originated because heads of the plant were used to fill beds as a substitute for feathers. As described under Purple Everlasting (*Gamochaeta purpurea*, page 26), this plant is also called Cudweed. Sometimes known as Rabbit Tobacco from a Cherokee legend, the dried leaves were smoked in a pipe by the Rappahannock Indians for asthma.

Blooms August–October.

Helen Hamilton

White Oldfield Aster NATIVE

Symphyotrichum pilosum (Aster pilosus)   ASTERACEAE Aster Family

Description. This aster is a broadly branched perennial 1 to 3 feet tall. Flowering stems are long, with conspicuous needle-like leaves held erect or horizontal to the ground. The alternate, linear leaves are up to 4 inches long and ½ inch wide near the base of the plant, becoming much smaller ascending the stems. Daisy-like flower heads have 16 to 35 white ray flowers and centers that are yellow when young, later becoming reddish. The bracts around the base of the head are loose and pointed. The stems and leaves may be covered with tiny white hairs, giving a frost-like appearance.

Habitat. This aster is easy to grow, thriving in any soil with full sun and moist to dry conditions, and can spread aggressively by self-seeding. Also called Frost Aster, it is widely distributed over the eastern and central U.S. and Canada and grows in every county in Virginia.

Comments. Since White Oldfield Aster is one of the last plants to remain in flower before a heavy frost, it is an important source of pre-winter nourishment for many insects.

Blooms September–November.

Small-headed Aster   NATIVE

Symphyotrichum racemosum (Aster vimineus) ASTERACEAE Aster Family

Description. This late-blooming species of small-headed, white-rayed aster differs from other similar-looking species chiefly by its recurved flowering branches that have all the flower heads arrayed along one side of the branch. All these species are bushy, broadly branched perennials with long flowering branches. The common name Calico Aster has been applied to one species *(S. lateriflorum)* in reference to the centers of the heads first being yellow and later turning purplish-red, such that heads on one plant and even the flowers within a single head may include both colors at the same time.

Habitat. This aster is easy to grow; preferring full sun in moist to dry conditions, it can thrive in any soil and may spread aggressively by self-seeding. Widely distributed over eastern and central U.S. and Canada, this plant grows in every county in Virginia.

Comments. The genus name *Aster* is now generally restricted to the Old World species, and the New World species have been reclassified into 10 other genera. All but one of our Virginia species formerly classified in *Aster* are now under *Symphyotrichum* or other genera. The name derives from Greek *symphy(o)* "coming together," and *trich(o)* "hair," possibly referring to the coherent anthers.

Blooms August–November.

Mayapple

NATIVE

Podophyllum peltatum   BERBERIDACEAE Barberry Family

Description: The solitary, nodding white flower of Mayapple is concealed beneath a pair of large, deeply lobed leaves at the top of the stem. The leaves grow up to 1 foot wide and can form a continuous layer of green umbrellas across the forest floor. Flowers are 2 inches wide with 6 to 9 white petals, resembling apple blossoms. By midsummer a fleshy, yellowish, egg-shaped fruit about 2 inches long appears, still hidden by the leaves.

Habitat. Mayapples are found in rich open woods and damp shady clearings in every county in Virginia. The plant ranges from Quebec to Minnesota and south to Florida and Texas.

Comments. Linnaeus saw a similarity between the leaf and a duck's foot and so called it foot-leaf, *podos* being Greek for "foot" and *phyllon* meaning "leaf." Or *Podophyllum* may refer to the stoutness of the petioles. The fruit is edible when ripe, but all other parts of the plant, apparently including the seeds, are toxic when eaten with abandon, and repeated skin exposure to the resin can lead to death. The roots produce a toxic action on cell division and have been used in anticancer therapies. Native Americans made an insecticide from powdered roots and used the plant medicinally against warts.

Blooms March–May.

33

Helen Hamilton

Mouse-ear Cress INTRODUCED

Arabidopsis thaliana   BRASSICACEAE Mustard Family

Description. One of a number of small, weedy, spring-blooming annuals called cresses, Mouse-ear Cress differs in its combination of leaves and fruits. The leaves are chiefly in a basal rosette, oblong to spatulate and hairy. Branching stems growing 4 to 18 inches tall bear tiny 4-petaled white flowers on slender stalks. The resulting fruits are very slender, ¾ inch or less long but 10 to 15 times longer than broad.

Habitat. Mouse-ear Cress is native to Europe, Asia, and northwest Africa. The plant grows in dry fields, roadsides, and waste places, especially in sandy soil, over much of the U.S. and Canada and in nearly every county in Virginia.

Comments. The scientific name comes from *arabis*, a Greek word used for "mustard" or "cress," and *thaliana*, honoring the plant's describer, Johannes Thal (1542–1583). Considered a weed in most areas, this fast-growing little plant is quite notable for its wide use in molecular biology, and is ideal for the study of plant development. Most tissues of young seedlings are translucent, aiding investigations into cellular activity. The genome of 5 chromosomes with only 115 million base pairs, among the smallest in the plant kingdom, was sequenced in 2000.

Blooms March–May.

Helen Hamilton

Sea Rocket

NATIVE

Cakile edentula   BRASSICACEAE Mustard Family

Description. Sea Rocket is a low-growing, succulent beach plant. The branching stems grow erect to 12 inches tall, often forming a zigzag pattern in the sand. Leaves are long, alternate, and somewhat spoon-shaped with wavy edges, turning yellow in the fall. The fleshy stems and leaves store water, helping the plant survive in a salty environment. Flowers have 4 white oblong petals. The fruits are unusual, distinctly divided into two unequal parts like a figure 8, the top part larger, plumper and 4-angled; the common name refers to their rocket-like shape.

Habitat. This is a plant of beaches, shores and dunes along the coast, typically in the wrack line with Russian Thistle *(Salsola kali)* and Cocklebur *(Xanthium strumarium)*. Ranging from Labrador to North Carolina and along the shores of the Great Lakes, Sea Rocket grows only in Virginia's coastal counties.

Comments. *Cakile* is an old Arabic name for this plant; *edentula* is from Latin *edentatus*, for "toothless," since the leaf edges are usually entire or wavy. Studies have shown that this species responds to burial in sand with enhanced growth and production of more seeds per plant. The fleshy leaves have a mild horseradish taste.

Blooms May–October.

Cut-leaf Toothwort

NATIVE

Cardamine concatenata
(Dentaria laciniata)

BRASSICACEAE Mustard Family

Description. This small plant is easily recognized by the whorl of 3 stem leaves, each divided into 3 or more long, narrow, jagged-lobed segments. The 6- to 12-inch stem is topped with a cluster of small white or pink flowers, the 4 petals arranged in the shape of a cross. Toothworts bloom in the spring before the leaves of deciduous trees appear. The common name refers to the tooth-like projections on the underground stems (rhizomes).

Habitat. The preferred habitat of Cut-leaf Toothwort is moist, rich woods, wooded bottomlands, rocky banks and bluffs, and limestone outcrops. Found in most counties of Virginia, including half the counties of the Coastal Plain, this plant is native from Maine and southern Quebec to Minnesota and south to Florida, Louisiana, and Oklahoma.

Comments. Sometimes known as Pepperroot, Cut-leaf Toothwort has a spicy, peppery root that has been used as a folk remedy for toothaches. It can be used as a condiment, mixed with vinegar and a little salt. Native Americans chewed the root for colds and gargled with root tea for sore throats.

Blooms March–May.

Helen Hamilton

Virginia Pepperweed

NATIVE

Lepidium virginicum BRASSICACEAE Mustard Family

Description. Tiny white 4-petaled flowers, usually with 2 stamens, are arranged in elongate clusters at the ends of the stems. The distinctive seed capsules are flat, roundish, slightly notched, and less than ¼ inch long. An annual or sometimes a biennial, Virginia Pepperweed grows 4 to 20 inches tall with erect, highly branched stems. The basal leaves are stalked and deeply lobed, while the leaves on the stems are toothed and lance-shaped.

Habitat. Growing in dry soil with full sun in fields, roadsides, gardens, and waste areas, Virginia Pepperweed is found in all counties of Virginia and across the U.S. The introduced species Field Pepperweed *(L. campestre)* is also widespread across Virginia and the continent, distinguished from the smooth-stemmed Virginia Pepperweed by its gray-green stems densely covered with long, fine hairs.

Comments. This prolific weed is one of the most common Pepperweeds. Its seeds have a peppery taste and can be used to season soups and stews; the young leaves are used in salads or cooked as greens. The genus name is derived from Greek for "little scale," referring to the fruit.

Blooms April–June, and sometimes throughout the year.

Sticky Mouse-ear
Chickweed

Cerastium sp.

Helen Hamilton

Sticky Mouse-ear Chickweed INTRODUCED

Cerastium glomeratum   CARYOPHYLLACEAE Pink Family

Description. Sticky Mouse-ear Chickweed is a low, weedy, often insignificant taprooted annual. The leaves are paired, oval, and hairy, hence the common name Mouse-ear. They are sessile on the sticky-hairy stems, which grow 6 to 18 inches long. Tiny white flowers ¼ inch wide have 5 petals cut so deeply that they appear as 10. The fruit is a conspicuous cylindrical capsule, pale and thin-walled, tipped with 10 minute teeth. The related Common Mouse-ear Chickweed *(C. fontanum* ssp. *vulgare)*, also introduced, is a perennial, matted at the base and rooting at the nodes. *Cerastium* species are very similar to Common Chickweed, *Stellaria media* (page 40), but the latter has short, ovoid, or oblong capsules.

Habitat. Mouse-ear Chickweeds grow in full sun to light shade and moist to slightly dry conditions, tolerating a broad range of soils, including those that contain clay-loam and pebbly or gravelly material. Native to Eurasia, often growing in lawns and other disturbed areas, these plants are widespread in Virginia and established over most of North America.

Comments. *Cerastium* is derived from Greek *cerastes*, "horned," referring to the slender, often curved capsules. The hairy leaves can be cooked and served as greens.

Blooms March–May.

Starry Campion

Bladder Campion

Starry Campion

Left: Phillip Merritt   Right: Helen Hamilton

Starry Campion

NATIVE

Silene stellata

CARYOPHYLLACEAE Pink Family

Description. This perennial bears deeply fringed, 5-petaled white flowers on tall slender stalks. The flowers are less than 1 inch wide, the petals flaring from a bell-shaped tube of united sepals. The long, lance-shaped leaves are mostly in whorls of 4 along the minutely pubescent 2- to 3-foot stems. The leaves of the introduced Bladder Campion (*S. vulgaris*, right) are opposite on glabrous stems, and the 5 white petals are deeply notched but without fringes. The base of the flower is papery, inflated, and net-veined, suggesting a tiny melon.

Habitat. Starry Campion grows in open woods and ranges from Massachusetts to North Dakota and south to Georgia and Texas. A native of Europe, Bladder Campion is now a common weed through much of North America. Both plants are widespread across Virginia.

Comments. The genus is named for Silenus, a mythical drunken Greek covered with foam; some species of this genus have sticky secretions and are called catchflies. A colonial botanist reported the use of Starry Campion for snakebite, suggested by the markings on the root similar to the skin of a rattlesnake, but found to be ineffective.

Blooms July–September.

Common Chickweed

Giant Chickweed

Phillip Merritt

Common Chickweed

Stellaria media CARYOPHYLLACEAE Pink Family

Description. The white flowers of Common Chickweed are very small, ¼ inch wide, with 5 deeply notched petals, appearing as 10. They occur in leafy clusters at the ends of weak, trailing stems to 16 inches long. The opposite leaves are broadly elliptic, the upper sessile, the lower leaves on petioles. A weedy annual, Common Chickweed flowers and sets seed continually. Giant Chickweed (*S. pubera*, right), a native perennial, is the showiest of the chickweeds, with beautiful star-like flowers more than ½ inch wide.

Habitat. A weed of waste places, cultivated areas, meadows, and woodlands, Common Chickweed was introduced from the Old World. It is found all over North America and in every county in Virginia. The native Giant Chickweed is less common in the Coastal Plain, more frequent westward in Virginia in rich woods and on rocky slopes. It ranges from New Jersey to Illinois and south to Florida and Alabama.

Comments. The genus name is from Latin *stella*, "a star." Common Chickweed is also known as Chickenwort because chickens and other birds will peck at the seeds. Chickens will also (eagerly!) eat leaves and stems of Common Chickweed. Tea made from this plant is a folk remedy for coughs and skin diseases.

Blooms all year; Giant Chickweed blooms April–June.

40

Phillip Merritt

Dodder

Cuscuta spp.   CONVOLVULACEAE Morning Glory Family

Description. Dodder is easily recognized by the yellow-orange stems that look like a tangle of thread. Lacking leaves and chlorophyll, these plants are parasitic on their host plants. Twining over and around clumps of perennial plants, dodders take nourishment by penetrating host tissues to obtain food and water. The seeds germinate in the soil, but the roots die as the plant twines around its host. Four species of dodder are found on the Coastal Plain in Virginia, distinguished by minute differences in the structure of their flowers, which are generally dense clusters of small white bell-shaped flowers.

Habitat. Dodder grows on a variety of hosts and is widespread across Virginia. The range is from Nova Scotia to Manitoba and south to Florida and Arizona.

Comments. The genus name *Cuscuta* is of Arabic derivation and means "dodder." This plant is also called Lovevine, since young maidens picked the vine and tossed it into weeds; if the vine had not attached to a host by the next day, her young man was not to be trusted. The stems were used by Cherokees as poultices for bruises, and the Chinese use the seeds of dodders for urinary tract ailments.

Blooms August–October.

41

Seig Kopinitz

Spotted Wintergreen

NATIVE

Chimaphila maculata   ERICACEAE Heath Family

Description. Spotted Wintergreen is well named, with its distinctive dark green leaves striped with white appearing just above the winter leaf litter. The leaves are pointed and finely toothed, wider toward the tip, and whorled or scattered along the stem. Growing no more than 10 inches high, the plant bears small white or pinkish, nodding waxy flowers with 5 petals (flower buds are shown in the photo) in a cluster on a slender stalk. The flowers mature into small capsules with seeds that are dispersed by the wind.

Habitat. This evergreen perennial grows in dry, often sandy, pine and oak forests. Found in every county in Virginia, the plant ranges from Maine to Florida west to Illinois and Mississippi and also occurs in Arizona.

Comments. This is not the edible wintergreen used to flavor candies—that species is Teaberry *(Gaultheria procumbens),* which grows in many counties of Virginia, most of them not along the coast. The genus name *Chimaphila* is derived from Greek *chima,* meaning "winter," and *philein,* "to love." The species name *maculata* means "spotted," referring to the pattern on the leaves, which are, however, striped, not spotted. Native Americans called this plant Pipsissewa, meaning "to make water," referring to how they and the American colonists used it as a diuretic.

Blooms May–June.

Indian Pipe   Pinesap

Indian Pipe

NATIVE

Monotropa uniflora

ERICACEAE Heath Family

Description. Lacking any green color, Indian Pipe is also known as Ghost Plant for its waxy-white, translucent color. Not more than 12 inches tall, the smooth (glabrous) stem is covered with scaly bracts (reduced leaves) and terminates in a single nodding flower. White or salmon-pink, the vase-like 1-inch flower has 4 to 5 petals, 10 to 12 stamens, and a single pistil. The fruit is an egg-shaped capsule that becomes enlarged and erect as the seeds mature; Indian Pipe turns black as the fruit ripens. This plant obtains nourishment from specific mycorrhizal fungi that are in a symbiotic relationship with the roots of trees, usually pines and oaks. Pinesap (*Hypopitys monotropa*, right) is similar but usually bears several flowers per stem. The whole plant is dull yellow or reddish but not white, and the stems are finely pubescent. The nodding flowers of both species sooner or later become erect.

Habitat. Both species are widespread in Virginia in mature, moist, shaded forests. The plants occur in most areas of the U.S. and Canada.

Comments. The genus name is composed of Greek *monos,* "one," and *tropos,* "turn," referring to the flowering stem that is turned to one side. *Uniflora* means "one-flowered."

Blooms June–October.

43

Phillip Merritt

Flowering Spurge

Euphorbia corollata   EUPHORBIACEAE Spurge Family

Description. The stems of Flowering Spurge grow erect to 3 feet, forming large, loose, flat-topped clusters of flowers. What appears as a flower is actually a cup with 5 white petal-like lobes around the edge. The cup contains many tiny male flowers and one larger stalked ovary that projects from it. The ovary produces 3 seeds, usually ejected mechanically. Linear leaves are 2 to 3 inches long and ½ inch wide with smooth margins. They occur alternately on the lower stem but further up are whorled, then opposite. When broken, the stems produce a milky latex.

Habitat. Preferring full sun, this perennial will tolerate almost any kind of soil, growing in dry fields and open woods and abundant in western prairies. Found in every county in Virginia, the species ranges from Massachusetts to Minnesota and south to Florida and Texas.

Comments. The flowers attract wasps, flies, and bees. Ants may distribute some seeds because of a small edible appendage at the base of the seed. The common name Spurge comes from Latin *expurgare* (to purge), and the plant has been used as a strong laxative, but large doses can be poisonous. The milky latex may cause blistering of the skin.

Blooms June–September.

44

Helen Hamilton

Spotted Spurge

Euphorbia maculata   EUPHORBIACEAE Spurge Family

Description. Spotted Spurge is a familiar creeping annual with more or less prostrate stems, often forming circular mats. The reddish stems are filled with a sticky, milky latex. Leaves are opposite, oblong, mostly less than ½ inch long, with toothed edges. Dark green, each often has a central purple spot. From the leaf axils, what appear to be very small flowers with four white petals anatomically are cups with petal-like edges containing several minute male flowers and one female flower each. This species can be confused with the widespread weed Nodding Spurge *(E. nutans)*, which has obliquely ascending stems and larger, asymmetric leaves.

Habitat. This is a common weed of open disturbed areas such as lawns, gardens, fields, and even sidewalk cracks. Found in every county in Virginia, Spotted Spurge is native over eastern North America and has been introduced elsewhere.

Comments. The milky latex can cause skin irritation and blistering and is toxic if ingested. The name *maculata,* "spotted," refers to the purplish mark on the leaf.

Blooms January–December.

45

Helen Hamilton

Sericea Lespedeza

Lespedeza cuneata   FABACEAE Pea Family

Description. Distinctive for its numerous wand-like leafy branches, this perennial grows to 4 feet tall on erect and somewhat woody stems. Tiny pea-like flowers, ¼ inch long, whitish or purple-veined, are in clusters of 1 to 4 between the stem and leaves. Compound leaves have 3 very small leaflets, narrowly wedge-shaped with blunt tips.

Habitat. Now a weed of roadsides, grasslands, pastures, fencerows, and fields, Sericea, also known as Chinese Bush-clover, is native to eastern Asia. The plant has been cultivated in the southeastern U.S. and planted along roadsides and in disturbed sites for erosion control. It ranges north to New Jersey and Michigan and is found throughout Virginia, mostly in the eastern and central counties.

Comments. The genus name honors an 18th-century Spanish governor of East Florida who was hospitable to the botanist André Michaux; *cuneata* means "wedge-shaped" and refers to the shape of the leaf. The leaves are silky underneath, hence the common name from the Latin *sericeus*, "silky." This invasive plant produces chemicals that inhibit the germination and growth of native vegetation preferred by livestock and wildlife. High levels of tannins make it unpalatable to grazers.

Blooms July–September.

White Sweet Clover INTRODUCED

Melilotus albus   FABACEAE Pea Family

Description. White Sweet Clover is an erect, branched annual or biennial growing 4 or more feet tall. The leaves are on stalks with 3 narrow, toothed leaflets, producing a sweet vanilla-like odor when crushed. Numerous tiny white pea-like flowers are in long racemes that tend to be somewhat one-sided. The fruit is oval, leathery and wrinkled, permanently enclosing the 1 or 2 seeds.

Habitat. Native to Eurasia, this plant is now established as a weed, especially in calcareous soil, along roadsides, in waste places, around buildings, and on back beaches. Ranging from Nova Scotia to British Columbia and south to Mexico and the West Indies, White Sweet Clover is found in every county in Virginia.

Comments. The scientific name *Melilotus albus* is derived from the Greek words *meli,* "honey" and *lotos,* "leguminous plants," and from Latin *alba,* "white." The plant is rich in protein; the young leaves can be eaten in salads or boiled, the seeds can flavor soups and stews, and the dried leaves have been used as a flavoring for pastries. Havasupai women dried the leaves and tied them to their clothing as a perfume. The plant is fragrant when dry and used as hay, but when improperly cured and moldy it can cause internal hemorrhaging and even death in livestock.

Blooms April–October.

White Clover INTRODUCED

Trifolium repens FABACEAE Pea Family

Description. White Clover often forms large masses in lawns from creeping stems that root at the nodes. These stems send up long-stalked, 3-parted leaves and long-stalked flower heads. The individual white to pink-tinged flowers are pea-like, no more than ½ inch long. The leaflets are finely toothed, nearly glabrous, with pale triangular markings.

Habitat. White Clover grows in open fields, lawns, and roadsides in every county in Virginia. A native of Eurasia, this perennial is commonly planted and has escaped to lawns and roadsides throughout most of temperate North America. A search in lawns may reveal an accidental four-leaf clover of this species.

Comments. The genus name *Trifolium* derives from Latin, meaning "3 leaves." *Repens*, the species name, means "creeping." This species and Least Hop Clover *(T. dubium)* are thought to be the Irish shamrock. White Clover is widely grown as a pasture plant, as it provides sweet forage for sheep and cattle, though sometimes reported as toxic. Many species of birds and mammals feed on the foliage, flowers, and seeds, and the flowers provide excellent honey.

Blooms April–October.

Helen Hamilton

Pennywort

Obolaria virginica   GENTIANACEAE Gentian Family

Description. Often hidden in leaf litter, this delicate little perennial can be overlooked until it achieves its 6-inch height. Pennywort is a low, fleshy, purplish-green plant with dull white or purplish ½-inch-long flowers, usually densely crowded in groups of 3 at the top of the stem and in the axils of the upper leaves. At the bottom of the stem the leaves are reduced to small scales; the upper leaves are opposite, stalkless, ½ inch long, thick, and round. There is some evidence the plant is dependent on mycorrhizal fungi for nourishment.

Habitat. Pennywort occurs in the Coastal Plain of Virginia and elsewhere in rich moist woods and thickets. The range is from New Jersey and Pennsylvania to Ohio, southern Indiana, and southern Illinois and south to Florida and Texas.

Comments. The common name refers to the coin-like shape of the leaves. Greek *obolos,* meaning "a small coin," provides the genus name.

Blooms March–May.

Water Horehound

European Bugleweed

Phillip Merritt

Water Horehound

NATIVE

Lycopus virginicus   LAMIACEAE Mint Family

Description. While Water Horehound is not fragrant, its square stems with opposite leaves mark this plant as a member of the Mint Family. Tiny white flowers are densely clustered in whorls in the axils of the leaves. Because the flowers have erect lobes and somewhat resemble a bugle, this plant is also known as Virginia Bugleweed. Dark green leaves are lance-shaped and strongly toothed, the lower ones with long, narrow bases. A perennial to 3 feet tall, it spreads vegetatively by numerous slender runners (stolons). Three other species are found in the Coastal Plain—American Bugleweed *(L. americanus)*, Stalked Bugleweed *(L. rubellus)*, and the introduced European Bugleweed *(L. europaeus*, right), all with small differences in their flowers and leaves.

Habitat. These plants grow in moist places and wetlands. Water Horehound is widespread across Virginia and ranges from Quebec to Minnesota and south to Georgia and Oklahoma.

Comments. Resembling the true Horehound *(Marrubium vulgare)*, these plants have been used as a folk remedy for coughs. The generic name is from Greek *lycos*, "a wolf" and *pous*, for "foot," referring to a similarity of some leaves to a wolf's footprint.

Blooms July–November.

Helen Hamilton

Beefsteak Plant INTRODUCED INVASIVE

Perilla frutescens LAMIACEAE Mint Family

Description. This is a distinctive annual with opposite, often crinkly leaves and a peculiar fragrance. The plant grows to 3 feet high, the small white to lavender 2-lipped flowers in long, spike-like groups from the leaf axils and stem tips. The ovate, coarsely toothed leaves are green when young, becoming partially purple. Also known as Purple Mint, the entire plant may be a bright purple mottled with red, like the color of raw beefsteak.

Habitat. This plant is native to the Himalayas and eastern Asia, now cultivated for its ornamental foliage and escaped into roadsides. It has become an invasive weed in the southern states and ranges from Massachusetts to Iowa and Kansas and south to Florida and Texas. Beefsteak Plant is found in most eastern and central counties of Virginia.

Comments. Beefsteak Plant is a favorite culinary herb in some Asian cultures, and the seeds are a rich source of an essential fatty acid. Considered a sedative, the leaves have been used in Asian traditional medicine for various ailments. A chemical in the leaves has caused severe lung lesions in mice, rats, and sheep. A variety of toxic effects and death have been reported in cattle and horses. The use in human foods and medicine is very controversial.

Blooms August–October.

Narrow-leaf
Mountain Mint

Clustered
Mountain Mint

Helen Hamilton

Narrow-leaf Mountain Mint NATIVE

Pycnanthemum tenuifolium   LAMIACEAE Mint Family

Description. Narrow-leaf Mountain Mint has a delicate, somewhat airy appearance. Very narrow leaves are hairless with prominent central veins and smooth margins. This native perennial grows 1 to 3 feet tall, branching frequently to create a bushy effect. Small white to lavender 2-lipped flowers are in dense clusters in the leaf axils or at the ends of slender, hairless stems. Clustered Mountain Mint (*P. muticum*, right) has much broader leaves, round at the base. The leaves near the flower clusters are whitened on their upper surfaces.

Habitat. This plant grows in dry soil of upland woods while Clustered Mountain Mint requires moist to boggy soils. Found in most counties of Virginia, they range over the eastern and central regions of the U.S. and Canada.

Comments. The genus name derives from Greek *pycnos* for "dense" and *anthemon*, meaning "flower," describing the crowded flower clusters, which attract many insects. *Tenuifolium* is from Latin *tenuis*, meaning "slender," referring to the narrow leaves. Mammalian herbivores usually don't browse on this plant because of the minty taste; the foliage may contain antibacterial substances that disrupt their digestive process.

Blooms June–August.

Helen Hamilton

Rose-mallow

NATIVE

Hibiscus moscheutos   MALVACEAE Mallow Family

Description. Rose-mallow is a perennial shrub-like herbaceous plant up to 6 feet tall. Large heart-shaped leaves are grayish green above and velvety-white below, producing a musky scent when crushed. The 5-petaled creamy-white flowers are large, up to 8 inches across. A band of deep red at the center of the flower surrounds the tubular column of yellow stamens. Existing in nature are numerous forms and petal colors ranging from pure white to deep rose, usually with an eye of deep maroon.

Habitat. Found in marshes along the coast and inland, Rose-mallow ranges from Massachusetts and New York to Ontario, southern Wisconsin, and Missouri south to the Gulf of Mexico, and sometimes escaped elsewhere. The plant grows in most counties of Virginia.

Comments. Rose-mallow has been used as a tea to treat digestive and urinary tract inflammations. *Hibiscus* is an old Greek and Latin name for marshmallow, *moscheutos,* because its odor suggests musk-rose. Cotton and okra are the most economically important members of the Mallow Family. Other members of the family produce a sap that, when whipped with sugar, was the origin of marshmallow candy.

Blooms June–September.

Carpetweed

Mollugo verticillata   MOLLUGINACEAE Carpetweed Family

Description. This creeping, glabrous annual is easy to identify, with its whorled leaves, tiny green and white flowers, and prostrate growth habit. The forked stems sprawl, and although the plant is small, it can form large mats, hence the name Carpetweed. The leaves are mostly narrow and unequal in size, appearing in whorls of 3 to 6, tapering to short stalks. The flowers are under ¼ inch wide with 5 white petal-like parts, arising on slender stalks from the leaf axils. The fruit is a tiny capsule with numerous red seeds.

Habitat. Carpetweed is widespread across Virginia, common on roadsides, edges of paths, and in disturbed soil, cultivated fields, gardens, and pastures. Apparently native to tropical America, it is now a common weed in moist soil and dunes nearly throughout temperate North America. The plant is listed as weedy or invasive in several states.

Comments. The genus name is derived from Latin *mollis*, "soft"; *verticillata* comes from Latin *verticillus*, meaning "whorl."

Blooms June–November.

Ellis Squires

Spring Beauty

NATIVE

Claytonia virginica   MONTIACEAE Montia Family

Description. Spring Beauty is a delicate ephemeral with loose clusters of star-like white to light-pink flowers, the petals lined with pink veins. While the flowers are less than 1 inch wide on thin stems only 4 to 6 inches tall, they are spectacular in large patches. Dark green grass-like leaves continue to grow after bloom and may eventually reach 9 to 12 inches in length before disappearing in late spring.

Habitat. Widespread in Virginia, Spring Beauty prefers organically rich, moist, well-drained soils in full sun to part shade. The plant ranges from Nova Scotia to Minnesota and south to Georgia and Texas.

Comments. Spring Beauty grows from an underground corm similar to a small potato with a sweet, chestnut-like flavor; Native Americans and colonists used them for food. John Clayton (1686–1773), who lived and worked in Gloucester County, Virginia, was one of the earliest collectors of native Virginia plants. His work was published as the 2-volume *Flora Virginica* under the auspices of the Dutch university professor J. F. Gronovius, who had him elected to the Swedish Royal Academy of Science. To commemorate Clayton, Linnaeus named the Spring Beauty in his honor. The local chapter of the Virginia Native Plant Society bears his name.

Blooms March–May.

Left: Jan Newton   Right: Phillip Merritt

Rattlesnake Plantain

NATIVE

Goodyera pubescens   ORCHIDACEAE Orchid Family

Description. This is a small orchid with a checkered leaf pattern and white flowers in a dense, elongate raceme (the individual flowers are stalked). The basal leaves are dark blue-green with a strong white midrib and a network of fine white lines; they are ovate to oblong and up to 3 inches long. Short scale-like bracts are present on the woolly flower stalk. The leaves persist through the winter and may last four years.

Habitat. Rattlesnake Plantain grows in average to moist soil in sun to partial shade. The plant is found in dry or moist deciduous (oak) and coniferous woods, often growing out of clumps of moss. The range is from southern Maine and southern Quebec to Minnesota and south to South Carolina, Georgia, Alabama, and Arkansas. It is widespread across Virginia.

Comments. The first part of the common name refers to the mottled leaves, which resemble a snake's skin, a similarity that once suggested their use as a snakebite remedy. "Plantain" is in reference to the broad rounded leaves, similar to those of plantains (*Plantago* spp.), common lawn weeds. The genus name *Goodyera* honors John Goodyer, an English botanist (1592–1664); the species name *pubescens* is Latin for "downy" or "hairy," referring to the downy hairs on the flower stalk.

Blooms June–August.

Louise Menges

Squawroot

Conopholis americana   OROBANCHACEAE Broomrape Family

Description. Looking like a mutant pine cone or corncob, this curious plant is parasitic on the roots of oak trees. Growing unbranched 4 to 8 inches tall, the stem is stout and mostly concealed by numerous fleshy, overlapping scale-like leaves. Flowers are formed on half or more of the shoot, densely crowded in a spike; the tubular flowers are ½ inch long, two-lipped, creamy at first, becoming brown. Each flower has 4 stamens with white filaments. Through the summer the flowering spike withers and becomes brown, persisting into the winter but shriveled and black. Squawroot spreads by reseeding itself.

Habitat. Without the need to photosynthesize, the plant can grow in deep shade to full sunlight in rich woods, dry to moist. Squawroot is more common in the mountains of Virginia than on the Coastal Plain, where it is found in northern and southern counties. Included here for its interesting habit, it ranges from Nova Scotia to Florida and west to Wisconsin and Alabama.

Comments. *Conopholis* is derived from Greek *conos*, meaning "cone," and *pholis* for "a scale," describing the shape of the plant and the appearance of scale-leaves. Other common names are Cancer-root and Bearcorn.

Blooms March–June.

57

Phillip Merritt

Beechdrops

Epifagus virginiana   OROBANCHACEAE Broomrape Family

Description. This interesting little plant is parasitic, attaching and receiving nourishment from the roots of beech trees. Growing 6 to 18 inches tall, its many-branched stems are pale brown, usually with fine brown-purple lines. Lacking chlorophyll, the leaves are represented by dry, brownish scales. Near the top of the stem are ½-inch-long tubular white flowers delicately marked with brown-purple stripes. The flowers lower on the stem are tiny and bud-like, never opening but self-fertilizing and producing abundant seeds. The fruit is a small ¼-inch brown capsule. Dried stalks often persist under the trees throughout the winter and into spring.

Habitat. Beechdrops grows in dry woods under beech trees in every county of Virginia. The range extends from Quebec and Nova Scotia to Wisconsin and south to Florida and Louisiana.

Comments. The plant is well named; *Epifagus* is derived from Greek *epi,* meaning "upon," and *phagos,* "the beech." A tea made from the fresh plant was once used for diarrhea, dysentery, mouth sores, and cold sores. Also known as Cancer-root, the plant was used in folk medicine as a cancer remedy, but recent tests for antitumor activity proved negative.

Blooms September–November.

Left: Teta Kain   Right: Helen Hamilton

Bloodroot

NATIVE

Sanguinaria canadensis   PAPAVERACEAE Poppy Family

Description. Growing 6 to 8 inches tall, Bloodroot is a spring ephemeral appearing for only a short time. In March, a brown tip emerges from the soil with a leaf inside. A satiny-white flower appears above the still-folded leaf. After the petals drop, the broad, orbicular leaf with 5 to 7 wavy lobes slowly opens. Once expanded, this leaf may shade the developing fruit capsule.

Habitat. Bloodroot is found in moist but well-drained woodland soil in all but a few counties in Virginia. In our area populations are somewhat limited to soils rich in calcium from fossil shells. The range is from Nova Scotia to Manitoba and south to Florida and Texas.

Comments. Bloodroot is named for the red latex extracted from the rhizome; the genus name is derived from *sanguinarius*, which means "bleeding." The root latex or powdered root can destroy tissues and has been used to treat conditions such as ringworm, warts, fungal growth, etc. Researchers are investigating its value in cancer treatment. An extract has long been used in toothpaste and mouthwash to fight plaque and gingivitis, a use now approved by the U.S. Food and Drug Administration. Native Americans used the latex as war paint and to dye fabrics.

Blooms March–April.

Left: Phillip Merritt   Right: Helen Hamilton

American Pokeweed   NATIVE

Phytolacca americana   PHYTOLACCACEAE Pokeweed Family

Description. This robust, branching perennial grows 3 to 9 feet tall, somewhat sprawling, with reddish stems. Loose columns (racemes) of small white or pinkish flowers develop into drooping clusters of glossy, purple-black berries. The leaves are alternate, smooth (glabrous), lance-shaped or somewhat elliptic, to 1 foot long.

Habitat. Growing on roadsides and in cultivated fields and waste places, this plant occurs from Maine to Minnesota south to the Gulf of Mexico, and in every county in Virginia. Widely dispersed by birds, it is abundant as a weed of urban, suburban, and agricultural disturbances.

Comments. The berry juice was used as a dye by the early colonists and to improve cheap wine. The young shoots were eaten in spring as cooked greens after two changes of water. Native Americans and early settlers found many medicinal uses for the plant. *Warning: All parts are poisonous, especially the roots, seeds, and mature stems and leaves.* The plant juice can cause dermatitis and can damage chromosomes if absorbed through skin abrasions. American Pokeweed contains a highly toxic chemical being investigated for anticancer and anti-HIV potential.

Blooms May–November.

English Plantain

INTRODUCED

Plantago lanceolata   PLANTAGINACEAE Plantain Family

Description. Also known as Rib-grass, this fibrous-rooted perennial has prominently-ribbed, narrow leaves 4 to 15 inches long. The strongly-grooved flowering stalks (6 to 24 inches tall) are bare of leaves and end with conic to cylindric spikes up to 3 inches long. The small whitish flowers are densely crowded, their large white anthers exserted on slender filaments. In Bracted Plantain *(P. aristata)*, with narrow, linear leaves, the bracts below each flower are long, bristling conspicuously from the spike, while the stamens (anthers and filaments) do not protrude.

Habitat. English Plantain, native to Eurasia, is now a cosmopolitan weed along roadsides and in lawns throughout the growing season. Originally native to the Midwest, Bracted Plantain blooms from April through July in disturbed habitats with dry, barren soils. Both species occur in every county in Virginia.

Comments. *Plantago* comes from Latin *planta* meaning "footprint," referring to the broad basal leaves of some species. With antibiotic and anti-inflammatory chemicals, English Plantain has been used to heal sores and for respiratory ailments. The seeds are eaten by songbirds and fed to caged birds.

Blooms April–November.

Helen Hamilton

Virginia Plantain NATIVE

Plantago virginica   PLANTAGINACEAE Plantain Family

Description. Virginia Plantain, also known as Dwarf Plantain, often grows only 4 to 8 inches tall and, unlike English Plantain (*P. lanceolata*, page 61), does not become a significant nuisance. An annual or biennial, most of the plant is covered with soft hairs. Narrow leaves 4 to 10 times as long as wide form a small rosette around the base. Unbranched flowering stalks end with cylindrical spikes densely packed with flowers. In contrast, Broad-leaved Plantain *(P. rugelii)* is essentially hairless, up to 10 inches tall, and with broad leaves under 3 times as long as wide. This perennial spreads by seeds, which can remain viable in the ground for several years. The fruit of all plantains is a capsule opening by a lid.

Habitat. Virginia Plantain is short-lived, whereas Broad-leaved Plantain blooms through summer and into fall (June–November). Both occur on roadsides and in lawns and disturbed areas in every county of Virginia and throughout the U.S. and Canada.

Comments. Many members of the genus *Plantago* are found all over the world. Some plantains are used in salads and as cooked greens. The laxative Psyllium comes from a species with mucilaginous seeds. Some are larval host plants to Buckeye and Checkerspot butterflies.

Blooms March–June.

Round-lobed Hepatica

NATIVE

Anemone (Hepatica) americana   RANUNCULACEAE   Buttercup Family

Description. One of the earliest spring wildflowers, this stemless plant has large basal leaves with 3 rounded lobes. Hairy flower stalks emerge from a tattered clump of leathery, burgundy-brown-tinted leaves from the previous year; new leaves appear only after the flowers bloom. Light blue to lavender or white flowers, easy to find in the forest litter, are 1 inch across on 8-inch-tall stalks. The flowers have numerous stamens and are without true petals, the petal-like 5 to 9 sepals surrounded by 3 bracts.

Habitat. Round-lobed Hepatica grows in dry or moist upland woods over most of Virginia. The range is from Quebec to Minnesota and Manitoba south to Georgia, Tennessee, and Missouri.

Comments. Widely used by Native Americans and colonists to treat many ailments, the plant served most commonly as a leaf tea for liver disorders. The common names Hepatica and Liverleaf refer to the leaves being 3-lobed (as is the liver) and becoming dark in color with age. Treating organ problems with the plants that most suggest them is known as the Doctrine of Signatures, an old superstition around the world in pre-modern cultures. Liverleaf may also refer to the brownish color of the overwintering leaves.

Blooms February–April.

Helen Hamilton

Thimbleweed

NATIVE

Anemone virginiana   RANUNCULACEAE Buttercup Family

Description. Growing up to 2 feet tall with 3-parted, deeply cut leaves, this spring-blooming perennial covers the ground through the growing season. White, 1-inch flowers with 5 greenish-white petal-like sepals appear above the foliage. The common name relates to the thimble-like center mound of yellowish stamens and thimble-shaped, cottony seed heads, which remain on the plants well into winter.

Habitat. Thimbleweed occurs in nearly every county in Virginia. It prefers moist, sandy soils and is easily grown in average, well-drained soil in full sun to part shade. Widespread in Canada and the U.S. except for the western states, Thimbleweed typically occurs in rocky or dry open woods or wooded slopes. The plant will quickly spread via underground stems (rhizomes), which produce vegetative offsets from the mother plant, and produces a chemical that inhibits development of other species.

Comments. Native Americans used root extractions medicinally, and to revive an unconscious patient, the smoke of the seeds was blown into the nostrils. Deer and rabbits usually leave this plant alone because the foliage contains a blistering agent that can irritate their mouthparts and digestive tract.

Blooms May–July.

Virgin's Bower

NATIVE

Clematis virginiana   RANUNCULACEAE Buttercup Family

Description. A fine-textured vine, Virgin's Bower features aromatic, pure-white flowers, each with 4 narrow petal-like sepals. Growing in clusters in leaf axils, the flowers are profuse enough to cover the foliage; the staminate and pistillate flowers are mostly on separate plants. In late summer the female flowers give way to showy feathery, plume-like seed heads. Without tendrils, the leaf stalks twist and wrap around other plants. Bright-green leaves are compound, with 3 sharply toothed or lobed oval leaflets each about 2 inches long.

Habitat. Virgin's Bower is easily grown in average, medium to wet, well-drained soils in full sun to partial shade. Occurring in moist low woodland areas and thickets bordering streams, ponds, and fence rows in most counties of Virginia, the plant ranges from Nova Scotia and Manitoba and south to Georgia, Kansas, and Louisiana.

Comments. Although toxic and irritating to the skin, the leaves have been used medicinally. The introduced Sweet Autumn Clematis *(C. terniflora)* has similar flowers, but the dark-green leaves, usually of 5 leaflets, are leathery, shiny, and smooth, without teeth or lobes. Native to Japan, this introduced plant is commonly cultivated, often escaped, and is considered invasive in some areas.

Blooms July–September.

Phillip Merritt

White Avens

NATIVE

Geum canadense

ROSACEAE Rose Family

Description. The 5-petaled flowers of White Avens resemble those of blackberries, but are smaller, the petals usually about ½ inch long and exceeding the sepals. Typical of members of the Rose Family, there are many stamens in the center of the flower. The slender stems are up to 3 feet tall; the basal leaves are long-stalked, often 3-lobed or dissected; upper leaves are reduced.

Habitat. White Avens prefers light shade or partial sun, moist to slightly dry conditions, and a loamy soil in moist or dry woods and thickets. Widespread across Virginia, this plant ranges from Nova Scotia to Minnesota and North Dakota and south to Georgia and Texas. Adapting well to disturbed areas, White Avens can spread aggressively and is somewhat weedy.

Comments. After the flowers fade, they are replaced by bristly fruits with hooked beaks that can cling to the fur of mammals, feathers of birds, and clothing of humans, thus facilitating seed dispersal. *Geum* is the classical Latin name for these plants.

Blooms May–July.

Helen Hamilton

Wild Strawberry

NATIVE

Fragaria virginiana

ROSACEAE Rose Family

Description. Wild Strawberry has red fruits similar to those of the cultivated species but smaller and much sweeter. The flowers are white, their centers filled with a large number of yellow anthers. This plant is instantly recognizable as a strawberry, with 3-parted coarsely toothed leaves and a ground-hugging habit. Both leaves and flowers are borne on 6-inch hairy stalks in loose clusters.

Habitat. Common in patches in fields and dry open places in sun or shade, Wild Strawberry is found in every county in Virginia and throughout the U.S. and Canada. It will tolerate moderately acid soil. Reproducing by runners, this low plant is a good groundcover over the summer. The cultivated strawberry is a hybrid developed from this native species and a South American one.

Comments. The berries attract wildlife and the plant is a larval host for the Gray Hairstreak butterfly common in coastal Virginia. Native Americans and early settlers used the plant to treat many disorders. Rich in vitamin C, the berries were eaten for scurvy and gout. The dried leaves are also high in Vitamin C and have been used as a tea.

Blooms April–June.

Partridge-berry

NATIVE

Mitchella repens   RUBIACEAE Madder Family

Description. Paired shiny, dark-green leaves with the occasional red berry announce the presence of Partridge-berry in woodland litter. A creeping evergreen perennial, it has stems that can grow to one foot long, rooting at the leaf nodes and forming extensive mats. Also known as Twinberry, paired white 4-petaled flowers open at the tip of each shoot; by flowering time the two flowers are already partially fused. Both must be pollinated to produce the red, double "two-eyed berry," edible but tasteless. It remains on the vine until after blooms appear the following spring.

Habitat. Partridge-berry is usually found in dry, acid woodland soils from Nova Scotia and Minnesota south to Florida and Texas. This little plant grows well in rich, dappled shade and occurs in every county in Virginia. It is very popular as a terrarium plant.

Comments. Linnaeus named this plant *Mitchella* for his friend John Mitchell, a botanist who lived in Virginia; *repens* refers to the plant's creeping growth. The only other species of *Mitchella* is in northeast Asia. Native Americans found many medicinal uses for this plant; women took frequent doses during the few weeks before giving birth. The Cherokee used the berries as food.

Blooms May–June.

Solomon's Plume   NATIVE

Maianthemum racemosum   RUSCACEAE Ruscus Family

Description. This perennial is well named, with an arching stem ending in a branched, pyramidal cluster of small white flowers. There are 3 petals, 3 petal-like sepals, and 6 stamens in each flower. Solomon's Plume is a large plant, growing 1 to 3 feet tall and spreading from a long creeping rhizome. The large leaves, 3 to 6 inches long with conspicuous parallel veins and hairy beneath, are alternate in 2 horizontal rows. At the end of the season berries replace the flowers—they are at first green, speckled with red, and finally translucent dotted with purple.

Habitat. Solomon's Plume is widespread across Virginia, growing in rich woods and clearings in partial shade. The range is from Nova Scotia to British Columbia and south to Georgia and Arizona.

Comments. Formerly known as *Smilacina racemosa,* the genus name *Maianthemum* is derived from Latin *Maius* for "May," when the flower blooms, and Greek *anthemom,* "a flower." The species name *racemosum* refers to the raceme-like panicle of the flower cluster. This plant is also known as False Solomon's Seal. Native Americans used the roots and leaves medicinally and used inhaled smoke for insanity and to quiet a crying child.

Blooms April–June.

Left: Seig Kopinitz   Right: Helen Hamilton

Solomon's Seal

Polygonatum biflorum

NATIVE

RUSCACEAE Ruscus Family

Description. No other perennial has the graceful arching stem and often hidden pendulous flowers of Solomon's Seal. The stems are slender, 1 to 3 feet high, and unbranched; a row of elongate greenish-white bell-shaped flowers hangs underneath. Round dark-blue or blackish berries, usually in pairs, replace the flowers under the stem. Leaves are broadly lance-shaped or egg-shaped and smooth on both sides; they have conspicuous parallel veins and turn yellow in the fall.

Habitat. Growing in moist woods, thickets, and roadsides, Solomon's Seal is found in every county in Virginia and ranges from Massachusetts and southern New Hampshire to Minnesota and Manitoba and south to Florida and northern Mexico.

Comments. The rootstock, or rhizome, is jointed, and when an old stem breaks away, a distinctive scar is left that is said to resemble the official seal of King Solomon. The common name may also refer to the wound-sealing properties of the plant, as reported by Gerard in 1597. Native Americans and colonists used the starchy rhizomes as food, boiling the young shoots and grinding the rootstock for flour.

Blooms April–June.

Lizard's-tail

NATIVE

Saururus cernuus   SAURURACEAE Lizard's-tail Family

Description. No other plant growing in wet places forms these dense, nodding spikes of fragrant white flowers. Individual flowers are tiny, lacking both sepals and petals. The heart-shaped leaves are alternate on stems 2 to 4 feet tall; when crushed, the foliage has a pleasant aroma like that of sassafras. The plants grow from aromatic rhizomes, often forming large colonies.

Habitat. Lizard's-tail tolerates saturated soils with up to 4 inches of water. It is common in swamps, shaded marshes, and stream edges in Coastal and Piedmont Virginia. The range is from southern New England and southern Quebec to Minnesota and south to Florida and Texas.

Comments. Both common and genus names refer to the long, finger-like spikes of flowers that appear during the summer. *Saururus* is derived from *sauros*, meaning "lizard," and *oura* for "tail." The genus has but 2 species, this and one in eastern Asia, a distribution found in a number of our native plant genera, reflecting a complex geological past. Lizard's-tail contains several novel compounds with sedative effects. Native Americans used a tea from the whole plant for general illnesses and the root as a poultice for wounds and inflammations.

Blooms May–July.

71

Phillip Merritt

Early Saxifrage

NATIVE

Micranthes (Saxifraga) virginiensis SAXIFRAGACEAE Saxifrage Family

Description. With small, brilliant-white flowers and leaves restricted to a basal rosette, Early Saxifrage is easy to recognize in early spring. The leaves are ovate, 1 to 3 inches long, usually coarsely toothed, narrowing to winged petioles. Lengthening from ⅓-foot to 1½ feet as it blooms, a sticky, hairy stalk supports flowers in branched clusters, compact at first, loosening with age. Individual flowers have 5 petals and 10 bright-yellow stamens.

Habitat. Widespread in Virginia, this perennial grows in moist or dry open woods and on rocky slopes and rock edges. The range is from New Brunswick to Manitoba and south to Georgia, Louisiana, and Oklahoma.

Comments. *Micranthes* translates as "small flowers." The older genus name is from Latin *saxum*, meaning "a stone," and *frangere*, "to break," referring to the stone-like bulblets on the roots of some European species, thought to dissolve kidney or gallbladder stones, or to the questionable ability of the plant to crack rocks, since they are often found growing in rock crevices. The young leaves of some species may be eaten in salads or as cooked greens.

Blooms March–May.

Moth Mullein

Common Mullein

Left: Phillip Merritt   Right: Ellis Squires

Moth Mullein   INTRODUCED

Verbascum blattaria   SCROPHULARIACEAE Snapdragon Family

Description. In its first year, this weedy plant forms a basal rosette
of hairless, oblong, tapering leaves with toothed edges. The flowering
stem arising the second year has alternate leaves reduced upward and
loose terminal clusters of yellow or white 5-lobed flowers, often with
purple centers, on long individual stalks. Common Mullein (*V. thapsus*, right), also introduced, is a much larger plant, with densely woolly
foliage and stems. Its yellow flowers are crowded into a very dense,
wand-like terminal cluster.

Habitat. Both species are primarily weeds of pastures, hay fields,
roadsides, rights-of way, and abandoned areas. Native to Eurasia,
these biennials are now distributed throughout the U.S. and in every
county in Virginia.

Comments. *Verbascum* is the classical Latin name of these plants.
Moth Mullein gets its name from the fuzzy purple stamens, reminiscent of a moth's antennae. In earlier times, the dried stalks of Common
Mullein were dipped in wax or tallow and used as torches. In Europe
the flowers and leaves of this plant are used in cough remedies.

Blooms May–June.

Left: Helen Hamilton   Right: Louise Menges

Jimson Weed

Datura stramonium   SOLANACEAE Nightshade Family

Description. Trumpet-shaped flowers are white to pale violet, 3 to 5 inches long with 5 teeth around the rim, followed by egg-shaped fruits covered in short spines. Blooming during the night, they are pollinated by Sphinx Moths. This coarse annual grows to 4 feet tall, the foliage with an unpleasant heavy scent. Green or purple stems are usually smooth, and the large leaves, to 8 inches long, have shallow lobes and a few teeth.

Habitat. Growing in disturbed sands, dry soil, and waste places, especially around barnyards, Jimson Weed is found in nearly every county in Virginia. Naturalized from South America and widespread in temperate and warm regions, the plant is abundant in the southwest and locally northwest into southern Canada.

Comments. This is an infamous plant, once used as an intoxicant by the early Jamestown settlers and called Jamestown Weed, now shortened to Jimson Weed. British soldiers sent to put down Bacon's Rebellion in 1676 were reportedly ill for some days after consuming Jimson Weed as greens. Native Americans used the leaves on boils, wounds, and hemorrhoids. The plant contains an assortment of toxic alkaloids, some mildly narcotic and hallucinogenic, others dangerously poisonous.

Blooms July–September.

Horsenettle

Solanum carolinense   SOLANACEAE Nightshade Family

Description. Horsenettle is a coarse, deep-rooted perennial with 5-lobed, star-like white or pale-lavender flowers in short clusters; the stamens form a yellow cone in the center. Growing to 3 feet tall, the stems are erect, branching, and loosely covered with hairs and very sharp prickles. The 5-inch-long leaves have large teeth or shallow lobes, are hairy on both sides, and prickly along the veins. While the fruits look like tomatoes, green at first, and later yellow, *they are poisonous when eaten, and fatalities in children have been reported*.

Habitat. In every county in Virginia, Horsenettle occurs in fields and waste places, especially in sandy soil. Originally native to the southeastern U.S. up to Virginia and Kentucky, this weedy plant is now established north to Vermont, Ontario, and Minnesota and westward.

Comments. *Solanum* is a nearly cosmopolitan genus of about 1700 species, including the cultivated tomato and potato. The Cherokee used an infusion of the leaves for worms and poison ivy; an infusion of seeds was gargled for sore throat and taken for goiter. The cut berries were fried in grease and used for dogs with mange; crushed leaves in sweet milk were used to kill flies.

Blooms May–July.

White Vervain

Blue Vervain

White Vervain

NATIVE

Verbena urticifolia

VERBENACEAE Verbena Family

Description. White Vervain is a coarse annual or perennial often more than 3 feet tall. The opposite leaves are sharp-pointed, broadly lanceolate to oblong-ovate, coarsely toothed, and often hairy beneath. The slender flowering spikes are loosely arranged, the tiny white 5-lobed flowers often thinly spaced. Blue Vervain (*V. hastata*, right) has slightly larger blue-violet flowers in dense pencil-like spikes, and its lower leaves are often 3-lobed.

Habitat. White Vervain grows in thickets, moist fields, and waste places in every county in Virginia, ranging from Quebec to North Dakota and south to Florida and Texas. Blue Vervain occurs in damp thickets, meadows, and roadsides in the Piedmont and Mountain areas of Virginia and in a few counties in the Coastal Plain.

Comments. The genus name *Verbena* has an obscure derivation generally describing plants used as healing or sacred herbs. *Urticifolia* refers to the nettle-like leaves. The nectar and pollen of the flowers of White Vervain attract bees, various flies, small butterflies, and wasps. The seeds are eaten by songbirds, but the leaves are too bitter for White-tailed Deer. Native Americans used Blue Vervain as a "female tonic" and for fevers, coughs, and stomach and bowel complaints.

Blooms June–October.

Anglepod Milkvine

NATIVE

Gonolobus suberosus
(Matelea gonocarpa)

APOCYNACEAE Dogbane Family

Description. This twining perennial vine has large heart-shaped leaves, often twice as long as wide, with smooth edges. They are paired on hairy stems up to 10 feet long that exude milky latex when broken. Distinctive 5-petaled yellow-brown flowers with purple centers grow in clusters at the end of long stalks emerging from the leaf axils. The flowers have a strong vanilla scent. The common name refers to the milky latex from the stems and the sharply angled, smooth podlike fruits.

Habitat. Anglepod Milkvine climbs on twigs and shrubs in shady moist woods and thickets in southeastern and central Virginia. The range is from Virginia to Florida and Texas and up the Mississippi embayment to southern Missouri and southern Indiana.

Comments. This plant was formerly in the genus *Matelea,* but *Gonolobus* is an older name. It is derived from Greek *gonia,* meaning "an angle," and *lobos,* "a capsule," referring to the angled fruit.

Blooms June–September.

77

Ellis Squires

Golden Club

NATIVE

Orontium aquaticum   ARACEAE Arum Family

Description. With a white stalk and a golden-yellow, club-like fleshy spike (spadix), Golden Club is a striking plant, especially when seen against dark waters. Tiny bright-yellow flowers with both pistils and stamens cover the spadix. Fruits are blue-green, one-seeded and berry-like. Elliptical in shape and borne on long stalks, the leaf blades are dark bluish green; their waxy, powdery surface renders them un-wettable, appearing silvery-glistening when forced under water. They will float in deeper water, but can be seen emerging in shallow water. Growing 1 to 2 feet tall, Golden Club will spread from stout, slowly creeping rhizomes (underground stems).

Habitat. The leaves of this plant develop best in full sun, but the plant will tolerate partial shade. Golden Club grows in marshes, swamps, and ponds in Virginia's Coastal Plain and elsewhere in the state. The range is from Massachusetts to Florida and west to central New York, eastern Kentucky and western Tennessee, and south to Louisiana and Texas.

Comments. The genus name is Latin for a plant that grows in the Orontes River of Syria. When properly prepared with repeated boiling, the rhizomes and seeds are edible, and the seeds were eaten by Native Americans.

Blooms March–April.

Helen Hamilton

Garden Asparagus INTRODUCED

Asparagus officinalis   ASPARAGACEAE Asparagus Family

Description. Garden Asparagus is a perennial plant growing to 6 feet. What appear to be leaves are actually clusters of very short, narrow branches, giving the plant a feathery appearance; the true leaves are tiny scales. Flowers are small, ¼ inch long, and appear as yellow-green bells hanging here and there along the branches. The fruit is a scarlet berry.

Habitat. A native of Europe now escaped from cultivation into waste places and along salt marshes, the plant is found in nearly every county in Virginia and throughout North America.

Comments. The spring shoots are a popular vegetable. The plant has been suggested as food for the treatment of gout, as asparagus contains at least 109 anti-inflammatory minerals or compounds. The use of the root is approved in Germany as a diuretic for irrigation therapy in the treatment of urinary tract inflammation and to prevent kidney stones. The seeds possess antibiotic activity.

Blooms April–May.

Tickseed Sunflower   NATIVE

Bidens aristosa (B. polylepis)   ASTERACEAE Aster Family

Description. This bushy plant features bright-yellow sunflower-like blooms near the top. Individual heads are 1½ to 2 inches wide, with 8 yellow "petals" (ray flowers) and a center disk about ½ inch across. The flat, one-seeded fruits may bear 2 to 4 barbed awns or be awnless. Opposite on the stem, the compound leaves are divided into 3 to 5 narrow leaflets. They are up to 4 inches long, pointed with coarse teeth, and may be further lobed near the base. Tickseed Sunflower is an annual or biennial, growing 1 to 5 feet tall. While the common name refers to "sunflowers," these plants have deeply cut leaves; the leaves of true sunflowers (genus *Helianthus*) are not divided.

Habitat. This plant grows in wet meadows, roadside ditches, abandoned fields, and low ground. Found all over Virginia, the plant ranges from Maine to Minnesota and south to Georgia and Texas. Crowned Beggar-ticks *(B. trichosperma)* is similar in appearance, with narrower fruits 2½ to 4 times as long as wide, but found only in a few eastern Virginia counties.

Comments. While Tickseed Sunflower is native to the central U.S., it may have only recently invaded and become established in the East.

Blooms August–November.

80

Helen Hamilton

Spanish Needles

NATIVE

Bidens bipinnata   ASTERACEAE Aster Family

Description. The common name comes from the long, slender, needle-like fruits arranged in round heads. The yellow flowering heads are small, ½ inch across, with only a few rays. These are weedy plants growing 1 to 4 feet high on erect, square stems. Leaves are opposite on the stem and fern-like, divided several times.

Habitat. Spanish Needles can be found in dry or rocky situations, on roadsides, in waste places, or as a weed in cultivated fields. This robust plant can adapt to a wide range of environmental conditions; disturbed habitats are preferred. Native to the southeastern U.S. and west to California and Mexico, it grows in every county in Virginia. Other members of the genus *Bidens* prefer wetter habitats, their leaves and flowers are different, and the fruits are broad, not needle-like.

Comments. The nectar and pollen of the flower heads attract bees. The genus name *Bidens* means "two teeth," referring to the barbed points on the fruits (commonly 3 to 4 on this species), giving them wide dispersal, as they will stick to anything passing by.

Blooms July–October.

Phillip Merritt

Showy Bur-marigold

NATIVE

Bidens laevis

ASTERACEAE Aster Family

Description. The striking yellow flower heads, indeed showy, are 2 inches across, and their disks have tiny red-tipped bracts among the florets. The toothed leaves are lance-shaped and lie close to the stem, more or less sessile. Showy Bur-marigold is an annual or sometimes perennial plant, growing 1 to 3 feet tall on smooth stems, simple or branched. This species produces one-seeded fruits (achenes) with barbed margins and 2 to 4 terminal awns, also barbed, which stick to clothing and animal fur, facilitating seed dispersal.

Habitat. Showy Bur-marigold is common in wet places, often in shallow water such as sloughs, ditches, freshwater and brackish marshes, and pond margins. The plant will tolerate clay soils if in full sun. In favorable years, it can form dense stands at the edges of ponds. Ranging from New Hampshire and Massachusetts to Florida and California, this plant is found only in the eastern counties of Virginia.

Comments. Showy Bur-marigold is attractive to bees, butterflies, and bee flies, which sip nectar and carry pollen, and to birds, which feed on the seeds.

Blooms August–November.

Jan Newton

Maryland Golden Aster

NATIVE

Chrysopsis mariana   ASTERACEAE Aster Family

Description. Maryland Golden Aster has a rosette appearance until late summer, when it sends up 12- to 16-inch stems displaying clusters of 1-inch golden-yellow, daisy-like flower heads. The stems and leaves are cobwebby-hairy early, but later become smooth. This species has a whitened midline on the upper surface of its leaves, making it distinguishable before it flowers from other herbaceous species with similar leaves. The "seeds" (achenes) bear a tiny double crown of bristles, the outer very short and scaly, the inner hair-like, bright tan.

Habitat. This native perennial grows well in full sun in dry, poor soil but tolerates light shade. Found in every county in Virginia, it is drought tolerant and easy to grow. Its range is from southern New York to Ohio and eastern Kentucky and south to Florida and Texas.

Comments. The genus name is composed of Greek *chrysos,* "gold," and *opsis,* "aspect," from the golden flowers. Maryland Golden Aster is not classified as a true aster because its ray flowers are yellow rather than white, pink, blue, or purple, as in members of the genera of true asters (*Symphyotrichum* and others).

Blooms June–October.

Lance-leaved
Tickseed

Threadleaf
Tickseed

Left: Helen Hamilton   Right: Seig Kopinitz

Lance-leaved Tickseed   NATIVE

Coreopsis lanceolata   ASTERACEAE Aster Family

Description. From late spring into summer, masses of bright yellow
flowers 1 to 2 inches wide cover this plant. Each flower head has 8 rays
toothed at the tips and flat yellow central disks. Fruits (achenes) have
conspicuous thin flat wings. The stems are leafy below, elongate and
leafless above. Leaves are mostly opposite and lance-shaped, 3 to 6
inches long, usually without teeth. Tickseed is a vigorous, long-blooming, clump-forming native perennial growing 1 to 2 feet tall. Another
native perennial mainly on the Coastal Plain, Threadleaf Tickseed
(*C. verticillata*, right) is similar, but its leaves are divided into thread-
like segments. The introduced Golden Tickseed (*C. tinctoria*) is a
slender western annual with feather-compound foliage and small,
abundant yellow flowers maroon near the center. It escapes to the East
in disturbed areas.

Habitat. Lance-leaved Tickseed is found in open woodlands, meadows, and thickets in dry and often sandy soil over most of the U.S. and
Canada and in nearly every county in Virginia. The plant is drought
tolerant and self-sows readily.

Comments. Reproducing from rhizomes, these plants will outgrow
weeds and hold the soil.

Blooms April–June.

Slender Goldenrod NATIVE

Euthamia caroliniana (Solidago tenuifolia) ASTERACEAE Aster Family

Description. This erect perennial grows 1 to 4 feet tall with many-branched stems. Tiny golden flowers grow on the tips of the branches, forming a flat-topped floral spray. The leaves are alternate, pointed, very narrow (less than ¼ inch wide), and smooth on the margins. The tiny one-seeded fruits have fluffy hairs that aid in dispersal. The leaves of a related species, Flat-top Goldenrod *(E. graminifolia)*, are wider, more than ½ inch across.

Habitat. Growing in damp to dry, sandy soil, these plants are found in brackish and freshwater marshes, on roadsides, and in thin woods. Slender Goldenrod grows along the coast from Nova Scotia to Florida and Louisiana, including the central and eastern counties of Virginia. Flat-top Goldenrod blooms earlier, from August to September, and has a wider distribution, occurring over most of the U.S. and Canada.

Comments. The genus name *Euthamia* is from a Greek word meaning "well-crowded," referring to the dense flower clusters. Also known as goldentops, these two species were formerly placed with other goldenrods in the genus *Solidago*.

Blooms September–November.

Common Sneezeweed

Southern Sneezeweed

Narrow-leaved Sneezeweed

Left: Jan Newton Right: Helen Hamilton

Common Sneezeweed   NATIVE

Helenium autumnale   ASTERACEAE Aster Family

Description. Sneezeweeds have wedge-shaped deep-yellow flower rays, distinctive with 3 teeth at the tips, becoming somewhat drooping. As seeds develop, the central knob-shaped disk becomes a deep-golden globe. Forming clumps 2 to 6 feet tall, the plants bear alternate, lance-shaped leaves with few teeth. Southern Sneezeweed (*H. flexuosum,* upper right) has purple-brown disks and smaller leaves, and Narrow-leaved Sneezeweed (*H. amarum,* lower right) is an annual, much shorter and bushier with very narrow leaves. Also known as Bitterweed, it is notorious for surviving in overgrazed pastures and rendering milk extremely bitter.

Habitat. Common and Southern Sneezeweed grow in moist meadows and shores throughout Virginia; Narrow-leaved Sneezeweed occurs only in the eastern and southern counties. Common Sneezeweed ranges from Quebec and Minnesota and south to Florida and Texas and westward.

Comments. The powdered disk flowers and leaves were in the past dried and used as snuff, thus the common name Sneezeweed. While poisonous to livestock, the bright-yellow flowers attract butterflies and other insects which distribute the pollen, and birds feed on the seeds.

Blooms September–October.

Narrowleaf Sunflower

Helianthus angustifolius   ASTERACEAE Aster Family

Description. This sunflower is distinguished by dark-green, narrow strap-like leaves generally less than ½ inch wide. A tall perennial growing to 2 to 6 feet, the plant achieves a bushy form and is covered with bright-yellow flowers. The flower heads are 2 to 3 inches wide with purplish-black disks, similar to those of Black-eyed Susan.

Habitat. Growing in swamps and other moist places, bogs, and pine barrens, Narrowleaf Sunflower is found chiefly near the coast in the southeastern counties of Virginia. Its range extends from Long Island to Florida and Texas and inland to southern Ohio, southern Indiana, and southern Missouri.

Comments. More than 50 species of *Helianthus* are native to North America, about 20 of them occurring in Virginia. Common Sunflower *(H. annuus)* is the commercial source for flowers, seeds, and oils, much cultivated for garden use and widely used at bird feeders. The plant often escapes cultivation or occurs spontaneously from spilled seed, but populations do not persist for more than a year or two.

Blooms September–October.

Jerusalem Artichoke

NATIVE

Helianthus tuberosus   ASTERACEAE Aster Family

Description. Growing to a height of 9 feet, this perennial has stems that are very rough and thick, as are the ovate, coarsely toothed leaves. Attached by winged stalks, the leaves are opposite on the lower stem, alternate above. Golden-yellow flower heads are 3 inches across, with long, pointed rays.

Habitat. While preferring loose loam, moist soil, and full sun, Jerusalem Artichoke can survive in poor soil and partial shade and in areas as cold as Alaska. The plant grows wild in moist thickets and fields in nearly every county in Virginia and in most states in the U.S. Large, crisp tubers, often similar to a medium-sized potato, terminate slender runners from the base of each plant. An abundance of tubers will be produced in the fall before the ground freezes.

Comments. Despite its name, this plant has no relation to the city of Jerusalem and is not a true artichoke. "Jerusalem" was probably corrupted from the Italian *girasole*, for "sunflower," and true artichokes come from a different, thistle-like member of the Aster Family. Sold in some markets as sunchokes, the edible tubers are highly nutritious, containing no starch, but they do contain inulin, a form of soluble fiber reputed to help lower blood cholesterol and sugar.

Blooms July–October.

Left: Louise Menges   Right: Phillip Merrit

Rattlesnake Weed

Hieracium venosum   ASTERACEAE Aster Family

Description. The green, purple-veined leaves of Rattlesnake Weed are unmistakable at the base of the plant. They are ovate and often densely hairy on the margins. Small yellow dandelion-like flower heads bloom on long stalks in open clusters from leafless 1- to 2-foot-tall stems. The tiny, one-seeded dry fruits carry yellowish bristles.

Habitat. Rattlesnake Weed grows in dry open woods, thickets, and clearings in every county in Virginia. The plant ranges from New York to northern Georgia and west to Michigan, Kentucky, Tennessee, and Alabama.

Comments. The genus name comes from Greek *hierax,* for "a hawk," the source of another common name, Veined Hawkweed. The Roman naturalist Pliny reported the ancient belief that hawks ate hawkweed species to strengthen their eyesight. While relatively widespread, Rattlesnake Weed is reputed to be most common in areas where rattlesnakes occur. Another source of the common name is its use as a snakebite remedy. Powdered leaves and roots and teas have been used medicinally, and folk medicine considered the juice in fresh leaves effective against warts.

Blooms April–July.

Helen Hamilton

Hairy Cat's Ear INTRODUCED

Hypochaeris radicata   ASTERACEAE Aster Family

Description. A common weed, this perennial is easily identified by
1- to 1½-inch-wide golden-yellow, dandelion-like flower heads on
leafless stems. At the base of the plant, leaves very hairy on both sides,
toothed or more deeply cut, form a rosette. A few scale-like bracts line
the flowering stem, which bears 2 to 7 flower heads on long branches.

Habitat. Hairy Cat's Ear, native to Eurasia, is now widely established
in the U.S. and southern Canada, growing in roadsides, fields, and
waste places. It is found in most eastern counties and a few western
counties in Virginia.

Comments. The common name refers to the hairs on the leaves resembling the hair on the ears of cats. The plant is also known as False Dandelion, as it is commonly mistaken for the true dandelions (*Taraxacum*
spp.*)*. Both plants carry similar flowers, which form windborne seeds
with plume-like bristles. Both have a rosette of leaves, milky juice, and
a central taproot. The flowering stems of Hairy Cat's Ear, however, are
solid and branching, while those of dandelions are hollow with a single
head at the tip. The leaves of dandelions may be more jaggedly cut, but
are much less hairy than those of Hairy Cat's Ear.

Blooms April–July.

Dwarf Dandelion   NATIVE

Krigia virginica   ASTERACEAE Aster Family

Description. This annual plant looks like a miniature dandelion, growing only one foot tall. The stems are leafless, or leafy only near the base, contain a milky latex, and arise from a cluster of 4-inch-long light-green basal leaves. These long, narrow leaves are somewhat hairy and pointed, with shallow, irregular lobes. The flower heads are small, less than 1 inch across, borne on long stalks, and composed of all ray flowers, bright golden-yellow and strap-like. The tips of the rays are flat and cut into 3 to 5 shallow segments. Dry seeds (achenes) crowned by 5 bristles and 5 tiny scales (lower right) are distributed by the wind. A clump of fibrous roots rather than a taproot anchors the plant.

Habitat. Dwarf Dandelion occurs in dry, poor soils, roadsides, fields, lawns, and sandy places. It grows best in full sun, acidic soils, and often disturbed areas. The plant is widespread across Virginia and ranges from Maine and Vermont to Wisconsin and south to Florida and Texas.

Comments. The genus name honors David Krig (or Krieg), a German physician who was among the first to collect plants in Maryland.

Blooms March–June.

Golden Ragwort

NATIVE

Packera aurea   ASTERACEAE Aster Family

Description. A welcome sign of spring, large clumps of Golden Ragwort cover swampy areas with bright-yellow blossoms on 1- to 2-foot stems. Heart-shaped basal leaves, usually purple beneath, persist to form groundcover over the winter. Stem leaves are reduced and narrow, more or less pinnately cut. The basal leaves of Woolly Ragwort *(P. tomentosa)* remain woolly below, are narrow and abruptly contract to the petiole. Small's Ragwort *(P. anonyma)* has nearly hairless, long tapering leaves and very numerous small, flowering heads. Unlike Woolly Ragwort, its larger stem leaves are deeply pinnately cut. All three species have yellow heads in flat-topped clusters and dry one-seeded fruits crowned with fine white hairs.

Habitat. Woolly and Small's Ragwort grow in dry open places, while Golden Ragwort is found in moist woods and swamps. Golden and Small's Ragwort are widespread across Virginia and the eastern U.S. Woolly Ragwort is limited to the southern counties in the Coastal Plain in Virginia and ranges from New Jersey to Florida and Texas.

Comments. "Ragwort" means a plant with ragged-cut leaves. These plants were formerly included in genus *Senecio*, which when broadly defined includes several thousand species.

Blooms March–June.

Narrowleaf Silkgrass

NATIVE

Pityopsis (Heterotheca) graminifolia   ASTERACEAE Aster Family

Description. This small aster-like flower is easy to overlook and sometimes mistaken for a grass. The 2-foot-tall stems are topped by clusters of bright-yellow, daisy-like flowers. Unlike true asters, both the ray and disk flowers are yellow. Small gray-green leaves are closely appressed to the stem, while those around the base of the plant are long and grass-like. The stem and leaves are covered with silvery-silky hairs, hence the common name.

Habitat. Narrowleaf Silkgrass is commonly found in dry places such as sandy woods, pine woods, old fields, and roadsides. This plant can form an evergreen groundcover and will survive heavy mowing, but does poorly in soils that are too rich or damp. It grows in the Coastal Plain in Virginia and in a few extreme southwestern counties, and ranges from Delaware to southern Ohio and south to Florida, the Bahamas, Texas, and Guatemala.

Comments. *Pityopsis* is derived from Greek *pity*, meaning "pine, fir," and *opsis,* meaning "appearance," possibly in reference to the habitat and flowering time of the plant. The species name is from Latin *gramineus* meaning "grass" and *folium,* meaning "a leaf," referring to the grass-like leaves of the plant.

Blooms June–October.

Helen Hamilton

Black-eyed Susan

Rudbeckia hirta

NATIVE

ASTERACEAE Aster Family

Description. Black-eyed Susan is well named for the 2- to 3-inch daisy-like flower heads with golden-yellow rays, often with reddish bases, surrounding a dark central disk. The heads occur singly on 1- to 2-foot stems, which are covered with bristly hairs, as are the coarsely toothed, oval leaves. This native prairie biennial generally blooms the second year, forming a rosette of leaves the first year. The disk flowers produce numerous small seeds prized by goldfinches. The Orange or Eastern Coneflower *(R. fulgida)* differs in minute characters and is less hairy, and the plants can form runners, sprouting new plants at their tips.

Habitat. Black-eyed Susan grows in full sun in various habitats. It is widespread across the U.S. and Canada and is found in every county in Virginia.

Comments. The genus name honors Olaf Rudbeck (1630–1702) and his son Olaf, professors of botany and predecessors of Linnaeus at Uppsala. Species names often describe characters of the plant. *Hirta,* "rough," refers to the hairy stems and leaves, and *fulgida* indicates the shining bright flowers. Many cultivars are available. Native Americans used root tea and juices medicinally. Like Echinacea, Black-eyed Susan has been found to have immunostimulant activity.

Blooms May–July.

94

Cutleaf Coneflower

NATIVE

Rudbeckia laciniata

ASTERACEAE Aster Family

Description. Cutleaf Coneflower grows 5 to 8 feet tall with large sunflower-like heads on freely branching, hairless stems. Also known as Green-headed Coneflower, it has greenish-yellow centers, which are unusual in this genus of the Black-eyed Susan. With golden-yellow rays, often reflexed, the heads can be 5 inches across. The lower leaves are usually deeply dissected, the lobes toothed, while those on the upper stem are much less divided. This perennial spreads rampantly by underground stems. Brown-eyed Susan *(R. triloba)*, with lower leaves often merely deeply trilobed, is 2 to 4 feet tall; short yellow rays surround a dark purple center.

Habitat. This perennial grows well in full sun and somewhat moist soil. It is found in rich woods, on streambanks, and in woodlands in every county in Virginia and is widespread across the U.S. and Canada. Brown-eyed Susan is native in only a few Coastal Plain counties in Virginia and occurs in the eastern and central U.S. and Canada.

Comments. The species name *laciniata* means "torn," referring to the deeply divided and toothed leaves. Traditionally the plant has been used to treat indigestion, burns, and other ailments.

Blooms July–October.

Helen Hamilton

Common Groundsel

Senecio vulgaris   ASTERACEAE Aster Family

Description. The flower heads of Common Groundsel generally lack rays, consisting only of a cylinder of small yellow disk flowers. While usually only 4 to 16 inches tall, this often hairy and weedy annual projects a very coarse appearance. The lower leaves are deeply toothed to deeply lobed, tapering to stalk-like bases, while the upper leaves clasp the stem. The slender wind-borne one-seeded fruits carry abundant soft bristles, giving fruiting colonies a cottony appearance.

Habitat. At present infrequent in all regions, this introduced weed is spreading across Virginia; Common Groundsel has become established along roadsides, in fields, on cultivated land, and on disturbed soils. The plant is native to Eurasia, now widely distributed through temperate North America from Labrador and Alaska south.

Comments. Members of this genus have been used as a yellow dye and contain an alkaloid *toxic to horses, cattle, and people*. The common name Groundsel has evolved from Anglo-Saxon "pus-absorber," and it was once used as poultices on wounds and abscesses. *Senecio* is derived from Latin *senex*, "an old man," alluding to the hoariness of many species, or to the white hairs at the tips of the fruits. Many attractive native species once included in *Senecio* have now been reclassified into the genus *Packera*.

Blooms March–June.

96

Helen Hamilton

Whorled Rosinweed

NATIVE

Silphium asteriscus (S. trifoliatum)   ASTERACEAE Aster Family

Description. An imposing meadow plant, Whorled Rosinweed produces sunflower-like heads well into the fall. Vibrant yellow, they are up to 2 inches wide with 12 to 20 rays. Only the ray flowers produce mature seeds (achenes). Lance-shaped leaves, usually on stalks, are in whorls of 3 or 4, occasionally opposite or alternate (mostly so in some varieties). Stems, often smooth and purple, reach 3 to 7 feet tall. Cup Plant *(S. perfoliatum)* is a popular garden plant, with its large leaves joined at the stem to form a cup that may hold water. Sunflower species *(Helianthus)* have mostly alternate leaves, and the disk flowers, not the rays, are fertile and produce mature seeds.

Habitat. Whorled Rosinweed prefers rich, well-drained soils in partial to full shade, spreading freely and drought tolerant once established. It occurs in open woods, prairies, and disturbed places. This species is widespread across Virginia and ranges from southeastern Pennsylvania to Missouri and south to Florida and Texas. Cup Plant is not native to the Coastal Plain, growing naturally in only a few southwestern counties in Virginia.

Comments. The common name Rosinweed refers to the gummy sap from broken stems that smells like pine or turpentine.

Blooms June–September.

Left: Helen Hamilton   Right: Phillip Merritt

Leafcup

NATIVE

Smallanthus uvedalius (Polymnia uvedalia)   ASTERACEAE Aster Family

Description. Leafcup is a large, coarse plant with stems often hairy above, growing 3 to 10 feet high. The very large leaves (to more than a foot long) are mostly opposite and palmately lobed, hence somewhat maple-like. At the base they often taper to conspicuously winged petioles, suggesting the name Leafcup. Typical of the Aster Family, the head of Leafcup consists of a central disk of small flowers with an outer ring of large petal-like ray flowers. There are 8 to 11 yellow rays, and the flower head is 1 to 3 inches wide overall in this species.

Habitat. Leafcup grows in rich woods, thickets, and meadows. Native to nearly every county in Virginia, the plant ranges from New York to Illinois and Missouri and south to Florida and Texas.

Comments. The genus honors John Kunkel Small (1869–1938), eminent author of works including *Manual of the Southeastern Flora.* An extract from the root is said to promote the growth of hair.

Blooms July–October.

Tall Goldenrod

NATIVE

Solidago altissima (S. canadensis)

ASTERACEAE Aster Family

Description. Blooming profusely in late autumn, Tall Goldenrod is distinctive, with tall plumes of golden-yellow flowers. The small flower heads are arranged along the upper side of the branches, forming a feathery, pyramidal plume. The plant can grow to more than 6 feet tall and will self-seed prolifically. The downy grayish stem bears leaves that may be toothed, are rough and finely downy beneath, and have a pair of prominent lateral veins.

Habitat. Tall Goldenrod can be seen along roadsides, in open woods, and in other dry, open places. This vigorous perennial is found across the U.S. and most of Canada and in nearly every county in Virginia. Requiring little care, Tall Goldenrod grows in any soil, dry to moist.

Comments. There are many widespread goldenrod species in Virginia, and some with restricted distributions. They may have flower heads in plumes or in arrangements that are branching, club-like, slender and wand-like, or flat-topped. Although goldenrods are commonly blamed for hay fever, this discomfort is usually caused by the pollen from ragweeds (*Ambrosia* spp.), which is wind-borne. The pollen of goldenrods is adapted to be carried by insects and is too heavy to become airborne.

Blooms August–October.

Helen Hamilton

Seaside Goldenrod

NATIVE

Solidago sempervirens

ASTERACEAE Aster Family

Description. Of the many goldenrods in Virginia, this is the only one with thick fleshy leaves that have smooth toothless edges. From a rosette of narrow, lance-shaped leaves, the firm stem with numerous narrow leaves may reach a height of 6 feet. A spray of bright-yellow flower heads in curved, one-sided clusters forms a large mass of blossoms at the ends of stems.

Habitat. This is a plant of marshes and sandy soil near the sea, growing at the edge of salt or brackish marshes, on small dunes, and in meadows. Occurring only in the Coastal Plain in Virginia, Seaside Goldenrod is found in salty places along the coast from the Gulf of St. Lawrence to tropical America. The plant has spread inland locally, especially along highways that are salted in winter, reportedly even as far west as Michigan.

Comments. Species of goldenrod were used by Native Americans for toothaches, colds, heart disease, sore throat, fevers, cramps, and internal hemorrhage. When the Omaha were on the summer buffalo hunt, the sight of goldenrod indicated that their corn was beginning to ripen at home. The name comes from Latin *solidus* and *ago*, which both mean "to make whole," because this group of plants supposedly heals wounds.

Blooms August–November.

Helen Hamilton

Common Dandelion

Taraxacum officinale   ASTERACEAE Aster Family

Description. Common Dandelion is a familiar perennial weed with a long taproot and milky juice. The leaves are all in a rosette around the base, long and deeply divided or lobed, sometimes hairy. With no central disk flowers, the large handsome yellow flower heads are composed of ray florets. Each head is carried at the tip of an unbranched hollow stem arising from the base of the plant. The seeds (achenes) are brownish and have a long thin neck, at the top of which is a "parachute" (pappus) of numerous fine bristles. The familiar, airy ball of seeds is easily disrupted and the seeds broadcast on the wind.

Habitat. Naturalized from Eurasia, this plant is now a cosmopolitan weed of temperate climates. It occurs in every county in Virginia, along roadsides, in fields and lawns, and on disturbed sites. Blooming most abundantly in April and May, it may be found in any month—in cool places in summer or in protected spots in winter.

Comments. The genus name is derived from Persian words for "bitter leaf." *Officinale* means "medicinal." The young leaves are edible, often collected in early spring for use in salads.

Blooms January–December.

101

Phillip Merritt

Yellow Crownbeard

Verbesina occidentalis　　　　　ASTERACEAE Aster Family

Description. With a flower cluster like a ragged yellow mop, Yellow Crownbeard is easy to recognize. Although related to sunflowers, this member of the Aster Family has only a few yellow ray flowers, usually 2 to 4, often bent backward from a center of small yellow disk flowers. The wide oval leaves, positioned opposite each other on the stem, have irregularly toothed edges and flow into "wings" on the stem. The plant grows to 6 feet tall.

Habitat. This plant is found in woodlands, fields, and pastures from Maryland and Missouri and south to Florida and Texas, and over most of Virginia. Yellow Crownbeard grows in sun or shade but requires soil that is consistently moist.

Comments. Yellow Crownbeard is attractive to bees, butterflies, and birds. This plant can be confused with Wingstem *(Verbesina alternifolia)*; the flowers are similar, but the leaves of Wingstem occur alternately along the stem. Wingstem is not common in the Coastal Plain, growing in the Piedmont and Mountain regions of Virginia.

Blooms August–September.

Helen Hamilton

Asiatic Hawk's-beard

Youngia (Crepis) japonica   ASTERACEAE Aster Family

Description. This annual weed is easily recognized, with a basal rosette of deeply cut gray-green leaves, hairy lower stems, and numerous small heads of bright-yellow flowers. As in its relatives hawkweeds and dandelions, the heads consist of petal-like ray flowers only, and the plant bears milky latex. The stems are 4 inches to 3 feet tall, arising from a taproot. Spreading by wind-blown seeds (achenes) crowned with abundant fine white bristles, the plant is rapidly invading the eastern U.S.

Habitat. Asiatic Hawk's-beard grows in gardens, roadsides, trail edges, and waste areas, and can move into minimally disturbed natural areas. It may grow in any soil, in sun or shade, and tolerates even heavy shade. Native to southeast Asia, it is now a pantropical weed, becoming common on the Coastal Plain in the southeast U.S. north to Pennsylvania.

Comments. The genus was named for William Young (1742–1785), a German-born American botanist, nurseryman, and gardener. The species name *japonica* means "of Japan."

Blooms April–June.

Early Winter Cress

INTRODUCED

Barbarea verna   BRASSICACEAE Mustard Family

Description. In early spring, fields are often covered with this 1- to 2-foot-tall biennial plant with bright-yellow, 4-petaled flowers. The dark-green leaves at the base are lobed and grow in a rosette formation. The upper stem leaves are smaller, feather-lobed or divided. Long, erect seedpods hug the stem. This plant is also known as Land Cress or Upland Cress for its similarity to Watercress *(Nasturtium officinale)*. Seed catalogs offer many cultivars of this plant for home vegetable gardening.

Habitat. Native to Eurasia and now naturalized in damp soil, fields, and roadsides, Early Winter Cress is found in nearly every county in Virginia and ranges from Newfoundland to Washington and south to Florida and California.

Comments. Considered a satisfactory substitute for Watercress, Early Winter Cress has been cultivated as a leaf vegetable in England since the 17th century. It can be used in sandwiches and salads or cooked like spinach. Although high in Vitamin C, the leaves have a hot, spicy watercress flavor when raw and are generally used in small amounts.

Blooms March–June.

Phillip Merritt

Eastern Prickly-pear

Opuntia humifusa   CACTACEAE Cactus Family

Description. This showy native perennial is the only cactus wide-spread in the East. The jointed stems are modified into flat, fleshy green pads that have large spines and tufts of tiny barbed bristles. Yellow flowers, often with reddish centers, are 3 inches wide with numerous sepals, petals, and stamens. Eastern Prickly-pear grows in clumps and often forms mats 3 feet wide and 1 foot tall. The sweet, juicy egg-shaped fruits, reddish-purple and 2 to 3 inches long with ruby-red pulp, taste a little like watermelon. This plant will root easily from pads placed on the ground.

Habitat. Eastern Prickly-pear needs full sun and dry soil; it is drought tolerant but will not survive soggy conditions. Common in dry open areas such as thin woods, dunes, and sandy prairies in the Coastal Plain of Virginia, it is scattered in other counties. The range is from Massachusetts and southern Minnesota and south to Florida and Texas.

Comments. Native Americans applied peeled pads to wounds and drank pad tea for lung ailments. Fruits were eaten fresh or dried for winter use. Today in the Southwest young Prickly-pear pads are sliced and boiled, tasting like green beans.

Blooms May–June.

Kathi Mestayer

Perfoliate Bellwort

Uvularia perfoliata   COLCHICACEAE Meadow Saffron Family

Description. Well named, its pale-yellow drooping flower is borne on a short stalk that appears to pierce a leaf-like bract. The 1-inch flowers are fragrant, narrowly bell-shaped with 3 petals, 3 petal-like sepals, and 6 stamens. The interior surface of the flower is roughened with small orange glands. The oblong or elliptical leaves also appear pierced near the base by the "perfoliate" stems. They are 2 to 3 inches long, usually hairless and somewhat whitened. Arising from a slender rhizome, the forked stem is under 1½ feet tall at flowering time. The leaves of the closely related Straw-lily *(U. sessilifolia)* are sessile and do not surround the stem.

Habitat. Also called Merrybells, these perennials prefer acid soils in moist to fairly dry hardwood forests. Both are widespread across Virginia. Perfoliate Bellwort ranges from New Hampshire to southern Ontario and Ohio and south to Georgia, western Florida, and east Texas. Straw-lily has a wider distribution, occurring in the eastern and central U.S. and Canada.

Comments. The genus name, from the Latin for "little grape," refers to the uvula, the fleshy lobe hanging at the back of the palate, and apparently to the drooping flowers of this genus.

Blooms April–May.

Helen Hamilton

Creeping Cucumber

NATIVE

Melothria pendula   CUCURBITACEAE Gourd Family

Description. This is a slender perennial vine climbing to 6 feet. The leaves are alternate, 5-lobed with smooth edges, and heart-shaped at the base; a tendril often develops from the stem beside each leaf stalk. Yellow flowers, usually unisexual, are borne on long stalks from the axils of the leaves. Male flowers are in clusters, bell-shaped, with 3 stamens; female flowers are one or few and wheel-shaped. The ovoid fruits ("melonettes") are ¾ inch or less long and often striped "like a baby watermelon" before turning dark. They contain numerous white seeds.

Habitat. Creeping Cucumber grows in woods, fields, thickets, and marshes, becoming weedy in disturbed areas such as roadsides and fields. This vine occurs in eastern counties of Virginia and ranges from southern Virginia, southern Indiana, and southern Missouri to Florida and throughout the American tropics.

Comments. The origin of the genus name is obscure; *pendula* refers to the little fruits that hang from the vine. The raw berries are edible but a drastic laxative, and they are considered mildly toxic.

Blooms June–November.

Left and right: Phillip Merritt   Center: Seig Kopinitz

Wild Yam

NATIVE

Dioscorea villosa   DIOSCOREACEAE Yam Family

Description. Wild Yam is a low, twining perennial vine, with lower leaves whorled and upper leaves alternate. The leaves are heart-shaped at the base, long-pointed, and with prominent, nearly parallel veins. Tiny greenish-yellow flowers hang in drooping spikes, the male and female flowers in separate clusters. Wild Yam can be recognized in winter by the dark brown, 3-winged capsules with very wide, winged seeds.

Habitat. Found in moist open woods, thickets, and roadsides, the plant will grow in poor soils and full sun. Known from nearly every county in Virginia, it ranges from Connecticut to Minnesota and south to Florida and Texas.

Comments. The genus name honors Pedanios Dioscorides, first-century Greek physician, whose book *Materia Medica* was the first illustrated book on plants and the ultimate reference for 1500 years. Native Americans used a tea made from its roots to relieve labor pains. Steroid hormones used in modern medicine, especially in contraceptives, were developed from components of the Yam Family. Although recently marketed as a source of estrogen or progesterone, Wild Yam root does not contain human sex hormones. The fresh plant may induce vomiting and other undesirable side effects.

Blooms April–June.

Slender Three-seeded Mercury   NATIVE

Acalypha gracilens   EUPHORBIACEAE Spurge Family

Description. This modest annual is also known as Shortstalk Copperleaf, since the leaves are on very short petioles up to ¼ as long as the blades and the alternate elliptic-lanceolate leaves often turn reddish in the fall. Stems are simple or branching from the base, to 2 feet tall and pubescent. The tiny flowers are in clusters in the leaf axils, surrounded by conspicuous leafy bracts with margins shallowly cut into 9 to 15 deltoid to ovate lobes. The fruit is a small capsule with 3 seeds. The leaves of Common Three-seeded Mercury *(A. rhomboidea)* are broader, their petioles ½ or more as long as the blades. These plants lack the toxic white latex characteristic of most spurges.

Habitat. Slender Three-seeded Mercury is found in dry soils of open woods, fields, and meadows from Maine to Wisconsin and south to Florida and Texas. This species and Common Three-seeded Mercury are widespread in Virginia.

Comments. The genus name comes from Greek *acklephes*, an ancient name for a kind of nettle, referring to the nettle-like appearance of the leaves; *gracilens* means "slender." Bobwhite Quail and Mourning Doves eat the seeds, and White-tailed Deer browse on the foliage.

Blooms June–November.

109

Phillip Merritt

Wild Indigo

NATIVE

Baptisia tinctoria   FABACEAE Pea Family

Description. Wild Indigo grows 2 to 3 feet tall, featuring numerous shoots with small, bright-yellow pea-type flowers. The sparsely-flowered clusters extend above a mound of foliage with stalkless, 3-parted gray-green leaves, the leaflets to 1 inch long. The flowers give way to small inflated seedpods that turn black and remain on the stem through late fall.

Habitat. Easily grown in average, well-drained soil, preferring full sun, the plant will tolerate drought and poor soils. Wild Indigo forms expanding clumps over time with deep and extensive root systems. It is found in every county in Virginia and its range extends from southern Maine to Georgia and Tennessee.

Comments. The showy flowers attract butterflies. Wild Indigo is sometimes known as Rattleweed because the seeds rattle around in the pods when ripe. Native Americans used the plant for various medicinal purposes, and studies have shown the extract stimulates the immune system. Wild Indigo was used by early Americans as a substitute for true indigo (genus *Indigofera*) in making dyes. *Baptisia* comes from the Greek word for "dye" and *tinctoria* is derived from the Latin word for "dye."

Blooms April–August.

Large-flowered Partridge Pea NATIVE

Chamaecrista (Cassia) fasciculata   FABACEAE Pea Family

Description. This straggly annual grows 6 to 30 inches tall with large
yellow flowers tucked in the leaf axils. The 5 petals are broad and
unequal, some with a red spot at the base. There are 10 stamens with
purplish anthers. Dark-green leaves are finely cut into 6 to 15 pairs
of leaflets, each tipped with a tiny bristle and sometimes sensitive to
the touch. Small-flowered Partridge Pea *(C. nictitans)* is similar, with
yellow flowers less than ½ inch wide and only 5 stamens.

Habitat. Partridge Pea is found in nearly every county in Virginia,
growing in a variety of open habitats. Preferring full sun, the plant
grows in average to dry conditions in soils of sand, loam, gravel, or
clay. The plant is easy to grow but can spread in poor soil where com-
petition is reduced from other plants.

Comments. Partridge Pea attracts bees and butterflies and is a nectar
source and larval host for several species of butterflies. The seed is a major
food item of Northern Bobwhite, and the plant provides excellent cover
for birds. Like other members of the Pea Family, this legume supports mi-
croorganisms that inhabit nodules on the plant's root system and produce
nitrogen compounds useful for the plant's survival.

Blooms June–September.

Black Medick

Medicago lupulina   FABACEAE Pea Family

Description. A weedy annual or biennial, Black Medick has hairy, branching stems that are low to the ground, to 2 feet or so long. Its leaves are compound, the central leaflet of the 3 stalked. The dense cluster of 10 to 50 yellow flowers suggests Low Hop Clover (*Trifolium campestre*, page 113), but in Black Medick, the petals are shed to bare the distinctive tiny, coiled, kidney-shaped black fruits. The related Alfalfa *(M. sativa)* is a perennial growing to 3 feet tall with purple flowers. Native to southwest Asia, Alfalfa may be the most important forage plant in the world, now spread and naturalized very widely.

Habitat. Native to Eurasia, Black Medick is common in fields, roadsides, and waste places. The species is widespread in Virginia, the U.S., and Canada.

Comments. *Medice* is the name of Alfalfa, as it came to the Greeks from Media (in Persia); *lupulina* means "hop-like," the fruiting clusters suggesting tiny hops. While the seeds of Black Medick can be ground into flour, Alfalfa is prized for the nutritious value of its leaves and seed heads. Both species are legumes and enrich the soil as the bacteria in the root nodules convert atmospheric nitrogen to usable forms.

Blooms April–August.

Helen Hamilton

Low Hop Clover

Trifolium campestre   FABACEAE Pea Family

Description. Low Hop Clover has 20 to 40 small yellow flowers in compact heads about ½ inch in diameter. This much-branched annual has sprawling hairy stems growing 6 to 18 inches long. The leaves are divided into 3 slightly toothed wedge-shaped leaflets, the terminal leaflet clearly stalked.

Habitat. Native to Eurasia and North Africa, Low Hop Clover is very common along roadsides and in fields, lawns, and disturbed areas. Found in every county in Virginia, it is established as a weed throughout much of North America.

Comments. The name *campestre* means "of the fields or plains." The dried petals persist and cover the heads long after flowering, giving them the aspect of small dried heads of hops, hence "Hop Clover." A close relative famous in Ireland, Least Hop Clover *(T. dubium),* is one of the shamrocks, potent charms against witches and fairies. Scattered throughout Virginia, Least Hop Clover has flowering heads under ⅜ inch in diameter with only 5 to 20 flowers. The flowers and leaves of Low Hop Clover can be eaten raw or cooked or drunk as a tea, and the dried heads can be ground into a nutritious flour. The tea can provide a calming effect and has been taken in the evening to help with sleep.

Blooms April–October.

113

Left: Helen Hamilton   Right: Phillip Merritt

Orangegrass

NATIVE

Hypericum gentianoides   HYPERICACEAE St. John's-wort Family

Description. Orangegrass is a conspicuous small plant, especially in late fall, with somewhat wiry, slender branches, burgundy-orange in color. Also known as Pineweed, its leaves are small and scalelike, pressed close to the stems. Tiny yellow flowers, nearly sessile, are scattered along the stems; they open only in sunlight. Very small red capsules line the branches after the flowers fade. This plant is an annual, usually only one foot tall, with the stem repeatedly divided into thread-like, upright branches.

Habitat. Common in bare, open sites, growing in sandy or rocky dry soils, Orangegrass occurs in nearly every county in Virginia. The range is from Maine and Minnesota south to Florida and Texas.

Comments. The Cherokee used Orangegrass to promote menstruation, for fever, to stop nosebleed, and as a snakebite remedy. When the eminent botanist John Bartram (1751) was thrown and kicked by a vicious horse, injuring both thighs, he boiled the plant and applied it to his wounds, appeasing the pain and hastening his recovery. He reported, "it is of excellent virtue, being made into an ointment...for bruises and strains."

Blooms July–October.

Helen Hamilton

Yellow Stargrass

Hypoxis hirsuta   HYPOXIDACEAE Stargrass Family

Description. Yellow Stargrass is easily overlooked, with grass-like leaves and small flowers. Star-shaped flowers have 3 petals and 3 sepals, all yellow and united only at the base. There are also 6 prominent stamens with large anthers surrounding a yellow pistil. The flowers occur at the tip of a hairy stem, often in clusters of 3, opening in the morning but wilting in the hot sun. Never more than 12 inches tall, the flower stalks are shorter than the long, narrow, somewhat hairy leaves.

Habitat. Yellow Stargrass is widespread in Virginia, growing in roadsides, meadows, and open woods with moist to slightly dry conditions. The plant can spread to form loose colonies but is not particularly aggressive. The range is from Maine to Manitoba and south to Georgia and Texas.

Comments. The genus name is from the Greek words *hypo*, "beneath," and *oxys*, "sharp," which may refer to the sharp-pointed tepals covering the fruiting capsule; *hirsuta* is Latin for "hairy." Traditionally included in the Lily Family, this small plant can be easily confused with a grass unless the flower is seen.

Blooms March–June.

Helen Hamilton

Yellow Trout Lily

NATIVE

Erythronium americanum   LILIACEAE Lily Family

Description. In early spring these bright-yellow flowers appear in wooded areas. Around the base of the stalk, the fleshy green leaves with purple mottling are equally distinctive in the forest litter. Growing only 4 to 6 inches tall on top of a drooping, solitary stem, the 1-inch flowers have 3 petals and 3 petal-like sepals, all curved backward. The petals have small lobes (auricles) at the base, there are 6 stamens with yellow anthers, and the fruit capsules are held erect. In the very similar, also widespread, Dimpled Trout Lily *(E. umbilicatum),* the petals lack auricles, stamens are usually brown or purple, and the fruit capsules lie on the ground.

Habitat. Yellow Trout Lily grows best in moist, acidic woodland soils; if left undisturbed, the plants will slowly spread into colonies by underground "roots" (stolons). The plant is found in most counties of Virginia and ranges from Nova Scotia and western Ontario to Minnesota and south to Florida and Alabama.

Comments. The common name refers to the brown- and purple-spotted leaves. Iroquois women ate the leaves to prevent conception, and the plant has antibacterial properties, but some toxicity.

Blooms February–April.

Left and top right: Seig Kopinitz   Bottom right: Jan Newton

Indian Cucumber

NATIVE

Medeola virginiana   LILIACEAE Lily Family

Description. Nodding yellowish-green flowers emerge above the leaves at the top of the stem on stalks that sometimes bend down below the leaves. There are 3 petals and 3 petal-like sepals, all bent backward. The reproductive parts are 6 stamens and an ovary with 3 long, brownish stigmas, curved back. An upright perennial, Indian Cucumber grows 1 to 2 feet tall on a slender, at first woolly, unbranched stem. Two sets of whorled leaves surround the stem, three at the top 1 to 3 inches long, and 6 to 10 larger leaves midway down the stem. As the dark bluish-purple berry is formed, the lower cluster of leaves turns red.

Habitat. Growing in eastern and western counties in Virginia, this plant prefers rich moist to wet soils in part to full shade. The range is from Nova Scotia to Michigan and southeast Wisconsin and south to Virginia and northern Missouri, in the mountains to Georgia and Alabama; also in Florida and possibly Louisiana.

Comments. The plant is often called Indian Cucumber Root for the crisp, edible rhizome, which can be eaten raw, its taste resembling that of a cucumber. Although Native Americans dug it for food, it is now scarce and the practice is not recommended.

Blooms April–June.

Yellow Pond-lily   NATIVE

Nuphar advena (N. luteum)   NYMPHAEACEAE Water Lily Family

Description. A hardy perennial, Yellow Pond-lily produces a globular flower with thick, succulent petal-like sepals and numerous tiny yellow or reddish petals and many stamens. The leaves vary from nearly round to heart-shaped, up to 12 inches wide and somewhat longer. In quiet waters, the leaves will float on the water's surface. Both leaf and flower stalks are of spongy tissue, often 2 to 4 feet long and extending from rhizomes sprouting in the mud. The plant also reproduces by seeds that burst from ripe leathery fruits, spattering them over the water surface, supposedly like those of dock *(Rumex),* hence another common name, Spatterdock.

Habitat. Found in ponds, swamps and sluggish streams, Yellow Pond-lily grows best in 1 to 3 feet of water in full sun to partial shade. Common in all areas of Virginia except the extreme south, the plant ranges from southern Maine to Florida and Cuba west to Wisconsin, Missouri, Kansas, Texas, and northern Mexico.

Comments. Native Americans consumed the starchy rootstocks as boiled or roasted vegetables and harvested the seed for grinding into flour. The roots were used medicinally but are potentially toxic.

Blooms April–October.

Seedbox

Ludwigia alternifolia   ONAGRACEAE Evening-primrose Family

Description. This plant is called Seedbox for the shape of the fruits: numerous cubical brown boxes no larger than ¼ inch across are filled with seeds. Growing 2 to 3 feet tall, the many-branched, smooth stems are covered with the fruits, especially visible in winter on the dead stalks. Lance-shaped leaves are alternate, tapering as they attach to the stem. In summer small yellow flowers with the parts in fours appear next to each leaf along the stem.

Habitat. This native perennial grows mostly in swamps and wet soil. With many seeds in each capsule, the plant can spread aggressively in the home garden. Ranging from Massachusetts and southern Ontario to Iowa and Kansas and south to Florida and Texas, Seedbox is found in nearly every county in Virginia. Two other species are common in Virginia: Wingleaf Primrose-willow *(L. decurrens)*, with larger flowers, 8 stamens and slender fruits about 4 times longer than broad, and Marsh Seedbox *(L. palustris)*, a prostrate or floating plant with opposite leaves.

Comments. Honored by the genus name, Christian Gottlieb Ludwig (1709–1773) was a professor of botany at Leipzig. The species name comes from the alternate arrangement of the leaves.

Blooms May–October.

119

Phillip Merritt

Evening-primrose   **NATIVE**

Oenothera biennis   ONAGRACEAE Evening-primrose Family

Description. Pale-yellow 4-petaled flowers, 1 to 2 inches wide with a
mild lemony scent, are in a spike-like cluster at the top of stems 1 to 6
feet tall. The flowers open in the evening and close by noon the next
day, thus encouraging pollination by moths. Somewhat wavy-edged
leaves are lance-shaped and slightly toothed. Seed capsules are long
and narrow, splitting open from the top to release many tiny, irregular
brown seeds small enough to be dispersed by the wind. The leaves of
the related Cutleaf Evening-primrose *(O. laciniata)*, are deeply lobed;
the plant is short, often annual.

Habitat. Evening-primrose is a biennial or short-lived perennial growing in fields and roadsides in every county in Virginia and throughout
most of the U.S. and southern Canada. Cutleaf Evening-primrose
prefers dry sandy soil and occurs in the Coastal Plain and Piedmont
regions of Virginia, and through the eastern U.S. to South America.

Comments. Both the roots and new leaves have been used in salads
or as cooked vegetables. Evening Primrose Oil is used in many cos-
metics, including lipstick. Native Americans used the root for various
ailments; recent research suggests that the seed oil may be useful for
eczema, asthma, migraines, and other disorders.

Blooms May–October.

Jan Newton

Sundrops

NATIVE

Oenothera fruticosa   ONAGRACEAE Evening-primrose Family

Description. This showy early-summer plant flowers in the morning and closes its blooms in the evening. The 4-petaled flowers are 2 inches wide and bright lemon-yellow; there are 8 prominent stamens and a large stigma deeply 4-lobed into a cross. Sundrops are erect plants under 3 feet tall with somewhat hairy, usually branching, stems. Lance-shaped leaves are up to 4 inches long with smooth to serrate edges. Seed capsules are club-shaped, under ½ inch long.

Habitat. Widespread across Virginia, this perennial prefers moist, well-drained soil in full to partial sun. The plant ranges from Nova Scotia to New York and south to Florida and Alabama.

Comments. The scientific name of the family is derived from *onager*, the Greek word for "wild ass," beasts who threw stones with their hind legs when agitated. The stone-throwing catapult, known as an onager, paralleled these plants, which fling seeds far and wide. The genus name *Oenothera* comes from a Greek word meaning "wine," since extracts from the roots of some members of this family were combined with wines. Enology (Oenology) is the science of wine-making.

Blooms April–August.

Yellow Wood-sorrel

Violet Wood-sorrel

Helen Hamilton

Yellow Wood-sorrel

NATIVE

Oxalis stricta   OXALIDACEAE Wood-sorrel Family

Description. Yellow Wood-sorrel is a familiar delicate weed with ⅓-inch, 5-petaled flowers and leaves with 3 heart-shaped leaflets that fold together at night. Its fruit is a cylindrical capsule to ½ inch or so long. Closely related, Slender Wood-sorrel *(O. dillenii)* is distinguished by small stipules on the base of the leaf stalk and it lacks the underground stems (rhizomes) of Yellow Wood-sorrel; names and species boundaries are very unsettled in the yellow wood-sorrel group. Two species with petals pink to purple or white are widespread in Virginia. Stemless, their leaves arise from a bulb-like structure. The flower peduncles and sepals are glabrous in the native Violet Wood-sorrel (*O. violacea*, right); they are pubescent in the introduced Red Wood-sorrel *(O. rubra)*.

Habitat. Both Yellow and Slender Wood-sorrel are probably native to North America but are now nearly cosmopolitan weeds.

Comments. The genus name comes from Greek for sorrel, *oxys*, "sour." The leaves are sour, containing oxalic acid. They have been used as flavorings and traditionally to treat a variety of illnesses such as sore throat, cancers, ulcers, fevers, and scurvy, but large doses risk oxalate poisoning.

Blooms May–October.

122

Whorled
Loosestrife

Fringed
Loosestrife

Whorled Loosestrife

NATIVE

Lysimachia quadrifolia   PRIMULACEAE Primrose Family

Description. With long-stalked yellow flowers arising from whorls of 3 to 6 leaves, these perennials, 3 feet or less tall, are distinctive. The flowers are 5-parted, red in the center, and less than ¾ inch broad. A related native species, Fringed Loosestrife (*L. ciliata*, right) has leaves opposite with long, conspicuously fringed (ciliated) petioles and larger plain yellow flowers. Native to Europe, Moneywort or Creeping Jenny *(L. nummularia)* is prostrate and mat-forming, with roundish leaves and large yellow flowers. It is often sold as a groundcover, but becomes weedy and invasive.

Habitat. Whorled Loosestrife prefers uplands, especially open woods, from Maine and Minnesota and south to South Carolina and Alabama. Fringed Loosestrife prefers moist soils in sunny habitats across Canada and much of the U.S. Both are widespread in Virginia.

Comments. The genus name comes from Greek *lysis,* "releasing," and *mache,* "strife"; King Lysimachos of Thrace was said to have pacified a maddened bull by waving a loosestrife plant. *Ciliata* comes from Latin *cilium,* for "small hairs," referring to the hairs on the leaf petioles.

Blooms May–August.

Marsh Marigold

Lesser Celandine

Left: Phillip Merritt   Right: Helen Hamilton

Marsh Marigold

NATIVE

Caltha palustris   RANUNCULACEAE Buttercup Family

Description. Bright-yellow blossoms with 5 to 6 ovate petal-like
sepals and numerous stamens grow above loose clumps of heart- or
kidney-shaped leaves. Stout, erect, hollow stems grow to 2 feet tall,
1 to 3 flowers on a stem. Very similar, the highly invasive introduced
Lesser Celandine (*Ficaria verna*, right) forms continuous mats of
growth, the flowers with 8 to 12 slender yellow petals.

Habitat. Marsh Marigold grows in wet meadows and woods, swamps,
bogs, and shallow water. The plant ranges from Labrador and Alaska and
south to South Carolina and Nebraska, also in Eurasia. In Virginia, the
plant has a disjunct range, occurring in the mountainous regions and on
the Coastal Plain, but not in the central area. Requiring calcareous soils,
it grows in ravine bottoms that have been downcut into shell deposits.
Lesser Celandine is becoming naturalized from horticultural plantings.

Comments. The scientific name is from Latin *calathos*, "cup," and
palustris, "boggy, marshy." When cooked, the early spring greens
are edible. The leaf tea is a diuretic and laxative. Ojibwas mixed tea
with maple sugar to make a cough syrup that was popular with the
colonists. In large quantities the leaves are toxic, and plant juices can
cause blistering of the skin.

Blooms April–June.

124

Kidneyleaf Crowfoot

NATIVE

Ranunculus abortivus   RANUNCULACEAE Buttercup Family

Description. Growing 1 to 2 feet tall in early spring, this little buttercup is easily overlooked, since the flower is no more than ¼ inch in diameter and drooping. Yellow petals and reflexed sepals surround a round head composed of many pistils and numerous yellow stamens. The basal leaves are kidney-shaped or round, heart-shaped at the base, and toothed. The leaves on the stem toward the flowers are narrow and divided.

Habitat. Kidneyleaf Crowfoot is abundant in moist or dry woods in every county in Virginia and widely distributed from Labrador to Alaska and south to Florida, Texas, and Colorado. Several other small-flowered buttercups occur in the Coastal Plain, differing in habitat, leaf, and fruit (achene) shape.

Comments. Latin *abortivus* translates as "abortive," referring to the reduced styles and petals of the flower. Often the members of this genus with larger flowers are called buttercups, whereas the small-flowered ones are known as crowfoots, referring to the divided leaves resembling a crow's foot. Buttercups contain varying amounts of an acrid poison that can cause intestinal irritation if eaten or skin blisters if handled. Cows poisoned by buttercups are said to produce bitter or reddish milk.

Blooms March–June.

Helen Hamilton

Bulbous Buttercup

Ranunculus bulbosus   RANUNCULACEAE Buttercup Family

Description. This common perennial lawn weed has silky-hairy stems growing a foot or so tall from a bulbous base. While the basal leaves are 3-parted, lobed and cut along the edges, the stem leaves are few and much smaller. The long-stalked golden-yellow flowers with broad shiny petals are about an inch across, with sepals bent down against the flower-stalk and numerous stamens and pistils. Fruits are one-seeded achenes.

Habitat. This European plant is now naturalized in fields, lawns and roadsides from Newfoundland to Georgia and to western North America. It grows in every county in Virginia.

Comments. *Ranunculus* is Latin for "little frog," the name applied by the Roman scholar Pliny because many species of this plant grow in wet habitats where frogs abound. This is a large genus, some members of which are acrid-narcotic, producing painful, deep ulcers and blisters. *R. bulbosus* has had a reputation as a powerful diuretic.

Blooms April–July.

126

Dwarf Cinquefoil

NATIVE

Potentilla canadensis   ROSACEAE Rose Family

Description. Also known as Running Five-fingers, Dwarf Cinque-foil has 5 wedge-shaped leaflets that are rounded and toothed only above the middle. At first the stems are short and erect, later becoming elongate and prostrate, spreading the plant by runners. With 5 bright-yellow petals and numerous stamens and pistils, the ½-inch-wide flowers bloom on long stalks from the leaf axils. The native Old-field Five-fingers *(P. simplex)* is very similar, but the leaflets are larger (2½ inches long) and have teeth along ¾ of their length. An introduced species, Sulfur Five-fingers *(P. recta)* is an erect, hairy plant with pale-yellow flowers; it becomes a noxious weed.

Habitat. Both native species are indicators of poor soil, growing in dry woods and fields and widespread across Virginia. Dwarf Cinquefoil ranges from Maine and Ontario and south to South Carolina and Alabama.

Comments. The genus name, from Latin *potens,* meaning "powerful," refers to the medicinal use of some species. Cinquefoil translates as "five" and "leaf." Native Americans made a tea of the pounded roots to treat diarrhea. Other cinquefoils are considered astringents.

Blooms March–May.

Indian Strawberry

INTRODUCED

Potentilla (Duchesnea) indica   ROSACEAE Rose Family

Description. Indian Strawberry is a small, creeping perennial, spreading by leafy runners. The basal leaves are long-stalked and divided into 3 leaflets with scalloped edges. Flowers have numerous stamens and 5 yellow petals. The back of the flower has 5 leaf-like bracts that are toothed and longer than the sepals and petals. This plant much resembles the Wild Strawberry (*Fragaria virginiana*, page 67), but the fruits are tasteless and flower petals are yellow, not white.

Habitat. Indian Strawberry grows in moist and shady places such as grassy areas and lawns and around buildings. Native to Asia, this weedy plant is established in moist waste places throughout Virginia and the northeastern U.S. It is often a pest in lawns.

Comments. Indian Strawberry and Wild Strawberry are not closely related, distinguished by two different genera, *Potentilla* and *Fragaria*. The older genus name is derived from an early cataloguer of *Fragaria*, A.N. Duchesne, and the species name refers to a possible origin in India. Whole-plant poultices have many uses in traditional medicine for burns, insect stings, and abscesses; the tea was used for laryngitis, coughs, and lung ailments.

Blooms February–frost.

Ellis Squires

Butterfly Weed

NATIVE

Asclepias tuberosa APOCYNACEAE Dogbane Family

Description. Definitely not a weed, this hairy, sturdy plant, 2 to 3 feet tall, bears wide, flat-topped clusters of vibrant orange all summer. The leaves are numerous, stiff, and lance-shaped, providing an attractive background of dark-green foliage for the showy flower heads. Unlike other species of *Asclepias*, Butterfly Weed has mostly alternate leaves and colorless juice, not milky latex. In autumn the seedpods break open to release ranks of seeds, each with a powder puff of silky threads, which the wind carries to new locations.

Habitat. Butterfly Weed is easily grown in ordinary well-drained garden soil, poor or rich, in sun or part shade, and is drought tolerant. Because of its long taproot, Butterfly Weed should be moved only as a young plant. This attractive perennial is found in fields, roadsides, and upland woods throughout the eastern, central, and southwestern states and in every county in Virginia.

Comments. Butterfly Weed is a favorite food source for both the larval and adult forms of the Monarch butterfly. Other butterflies such as Tiger, Spicebush, Black, and Pipevine swallowtails also eagerly drink the nectar. Bees use the plant for a food source and are important pollinators.

Blooms May–August.

Jewelweed

NATIVE

Impatiens capensis BALSAMINACEAE Touch-me-not Family

Description. A prolific blooming annual, Jewelweed has an orange flower with reddish spots that hangs like a jewel, with beaded water droplets glistening in the sunlight, hence the common name. Jewelweed grows 2 to 5 feet tall on succulent translucent stems. Thin, oval leaves up to 3 inches long are pale and covered underneath with a whitish powder. They are alternate on the stem, with wavy margins and long petioles. At maturity the capsules split open explosively when touched, suggesting the other name, Touch-me-not.

Habitat. Jewelweed grows in moist woods, on streambanks, and in wet roadside ditches in light shade to partial sun, preferring a fertile soil. The plant is found in every county in Virginia, ranging from Newfoundland to Saskatchewan and south to South Carolina, Alabama, and Oklahoma.

Comments. The crushed leaves and mucilaginous sap in the stems are a well-known folk remedy for skin irritations caused by Poison Ivy and Stinging Nettle; a component found in the leaves has anti-histaminic and anti-inflammatory activity. The flowers attract the Ruby-throated Hummingbird, bumblebees, and honeybees. Ruffed Grouse and Northern Bobwhite eat the large seeds and White-tailed Deer will browse on the foliage.

Blooms May–November.

Crested Fringed Orchid   NATIVE

Platanthera cristata   ORCHIDACEAE Orchid Family

Description. This is a very showy plant—a narrow, dense cluster of many yellow-orange flowers have drooping, deeply fringed lip petals. The back of the lip is prolonged into a spur ¼ inch long. While upper leaves are small, the lance-shaped leaves close to the base of the plant are up to 8 inches long. In a similar species, Yellow Fringed Orchid (*P. ciliaris*), the flower cluster is wider and more open and the individual flowers twice as large, with the projecting spur ¾ inch or longer. The two species sometimes hybridize.

Habitat. In Virginia Crested Fringed Orchid grows in acid soils in low, moist meadows and damp pine woods only in the counties of the Coastal Plain; its range is restricted to eastern and southern coastal states. Yellow Fringed Orchid grows in acid bogs, fields, and woods in the southern, central, and mountain counties of Virginia and has a wider distribution in the eastern and central U.S. and Canada.

Comments. *Platanthera* is from Greek for "broad" and "anther," referring to the unusually wide, flat anther. Orchid flowers often serve specific pollinators. It is reported that Crested Fringed Orchid favors bees, while the elongate spurs of Yellow Fringed Orchid can accommodate long-tongued butterflies.

Blooms June–September.

Phillip Merritt

Orange Milkwort

NATIVE

Polygala lutea   POLYGALACEAE Milkwort Family

Description. Milkworts have tiny flowers in small, 1-inch head-like clusters at the end of thin stems about 12 inches high. Orange Milkwort is a biennial with ¼-inch bright orange flowers fading to yellow. There are 5 sepals, the 2 lateral ones forming petal-like wings, and 3 petals united to form a tube. Stem leaves may be almost 2 inches long, while the basal leaves are broader, in a rosette. Several other species occur in the Coastal Plain. Both Maryland Milkwort *(P. mariana)* and Appalachian Milkwort *(P. curtissii)* are annual plants, with flower clusters pink to rose-purple.

Habitat. Orange Milkwort grows in sandy, acidic swamps and bogs, while the Maryland and Appalachian Milkworts occur in dry, sandy soil. All are well represented on the Coastal Plain, and Appalachian Milkwort extends to the southwestern counties. Orange and Maryland Milkwort range from Long Island to Florida and Texas; Appalachian Milkwort occurs from Delaware to Ohio and south to South Carolina and Mississippi.

Comments. Because their flowers superficially resemble pea flowers, Milkworts are often confused with members of the Pea Family. *Polygala* is derived from Greek *polys,* "much," and *gala,* "milk." Some European species were thought to increase milk production in cows.

Blooms April–October.

132

Teta Kain

Cardinal Flower   NATIVE

Lobelia cardinalis   CAMPANULACEAE Bellflower Family

Description. One of the few native plants with a true red color, Cardinal Flower produces just one elongate, densely packed flower cluster per stalk. The intensely scarlet tubular flowers open from bottom to top in the cluster and bloom for several weeks. In each flower the long gray stamens project through a split in the upper lip. In rich soil the plant will grow 2 to 4 feet tall.

Habitat. Cardinal Flower grows best in moist, rich soils in full sun to partial shade. The leaf rosettes must be open to the sun through the winter to ensure good growth the next summer. The plant will self-sow, and the seedlings can be transplanted in the fall or early spring. This perennial ranges from New Brunswick to Minnesota and south to the Gulf of Mexico, and is known from nearly every county in Virginia.

Comments. The flowers of this plant furnish nectar to hummingbirds and swallowtail butterflies. Since most insects find it difficult to penetrate the long tubular flowers, Cardinal Flower depends heavily on hummingbirds for pollination. The common name alludes to the bright red robes worn by Roman Catholic cardinals.

Blooms July–October.

Left: Jan Newton   Right: Seig Kopinitz

Pinweed

NATIVE

Lechea racemulosa   CISTACEAE Rockrose Family

Description. Pinweeds are small, scrubby perennials, usually no more than 1 foot tall, with stiff, wiry stems bearing narrow 1-inch-long leaves. Late in the season, basal shoots with many crowded leaves are produced. Numerous minute, 3-petaled red flowers open only on sunny mornings for a few hours. The small fruit capsules are twice as long as thick in this species. Easily overlooked, Pinweeds can be recognized by their feathery red stigmas and their presence on dry sites with few other plants.

Habitat. Growing in dry soil in sandy, open woods and fields, Pinweed is found in every county in Virginia and ranges from southeastern New York to Ontario and south to Georgia and Alabama. Two other species with broader fruits grow in Virginia: Leggett's Pinweed *(L. pulchella)*, in coastal counties and the Piedmont, and Beach Pinweed *(L. maritima)*, only in coastal areas and usually on dunes. Beach Pinweed is adapted to harsh conditions, with tiny hairs on the leaves that retard moisture loss and protect against solar radiation.

Comments. The common name comes from the small capsules that resemble the heads of tailor's pins. The genus name honors Johan Leche (1704–1764), a Swedish botanist.

Blooms June–July.

Sheep Sorrel

Curly Dock

Helen Hamilton

Sheep Sorrel INTRODUCED

Rumex acetosella   POLYGONACEAE Smartweed Family

Description. Low reddish- or yellowish-topped weeds massed on poor or sour soil call attention to Sheep Sorrel, or Sourgrass. A perennial from a creeping root system, its stems are about a foot tall and bear leaves commonly arrow-shaped, the two basal prongs spreading. Male and female flowers are produced on separate plants, but as in most wind-pollinated flowers without the need to attract insects, the parts are small and dull. Two related introduced species, much larger and coarser, are Curly Dock (*R. crispus*, right), with lance-shaped leaves, their margins often crisp and wavy, and Bitter Dock *(R. obtusifolius),* the leaves broadly oblong to ovate with red veins.

Habitat. All three species are native to Europe and are now weeds widespread across Virginia and throughout the U.S. and Canada.

Comments. *Rumex* is the ancient Latin name, and *acetosella* means "little sorrel." Young leaves of Sheep Sorrel are sometimes used as salad or potherbs in early spring. Widely used medicinally for a variety of ailments and rich in cancer-preventive vitamins, the plant can be poisonous due to high oxalic acid content. Species of *Rumex* are food plants for the caterpillars of copper butterflies.

Blooms March–June.

Left: Teta Kain   Right: Phillip Merritt

Eastern Columbine   **NATIVE**

Aquilegia canadensis   RANUNCULACEAE Buttercup Family

Description. Columbine is a beautiful woodland wildflower with showy, drooping, bell-like flowers. Numerous yellow stamens are surrounded by red petals and sepals extending backward into long hollow spurs with nectar-filled knobs, which are utilized by hawk moths and hummingbirds. Constrictions in the spurs prevent bees from reaching the nectar. Attractive in their own right, the compound leaves are divided into three segments, each with rounded lobes. The leaves are subject to leafminers, which do not seriously harm the plant. Columbine self-seeds, and young plants transplant easily in the fall.

Habitat. Growing about 2 feet tall in partly shaded to shaded woodland habitat, Columbine prefers limy soils. An early long-blooming spring plant, it grows well in filtered shade and will die out in rich, overly moist soil. This plant grows wild over most of the eastern and central U.S. and Canada and in most counties of Virginia.

Comments. The genus name *Aquilegia* comes from Latin *aquila* which means "eagle" and refers to the spurred petals that some believe resemble an eagle's talons. It is reported that Native Americans rubbed the crushed seeds on the hands of men as a love charm.

Blooms March–May.

Purple Pitcher Plant

NATIVE

Sarracenia purpurea   SARRACENIACEAE Pitcher Plant Family

Description. An unmistakable plant with pitcherlike, heavily veined red or green leaves usually half-filled with water. The flaring lips are lined with downward-pointing bristles, preventing escape of insects attracted to the colorful leaves and nectar inside. Falling into the water, insects are digested by plant enzymes and bacterial action, providing nitrogen to the plant. From the basal rosette of evergreen leaves resting on the ground, an erect leafless flowering stalk rises to a foot or so tall. Its solitary dull red flower is large, nodding, and globular, 2 to 3 inches wide. The pistil is very large and flattened, forming an umbrella-like structure in the center of the flower. Yellow Pitcher Plant *(S. flava)* is a taller plant with yellow petals.

Habitat. Pitcher plants grow principally in sphagnum bogs in Virginia, and only in the southeastern counties. The range of Purple Pitcher Plant is from Labrador and Saskatchewan to Florida and Louisiana; Yellow Pitcher Plant ranges from Virginia to Florida.

Comments. Efforts are ongoing to restore populations of both pitcher plants to historic ranges in Virginia and Maryland. Yellow Pitcher Plant is nearly extinct in Virginia due to development and habitat drainage.

Blooms April–May.

137

Swamp Milkweed

Clasping Milkweed

Swamp Milkweed   NATIVE

Asclepias incarnata   APOCYNACEAE Dogbane Family

Description. The deep-pink flowers of Swamp Milkweed top tall branching stems with opposite, lanceolate leaves pointed at the tips. Typical of milkweeds, the tiny flowers have 5 petals curving downward and a complex central crown. Thin, upright pods are produced, splitting open to release seeds attached to silky hairs that carry them on the wind. Also with deep pink-purple flowers, Clasping Milkweed (*A. amplexicaulis*, right) is so named for the pairs of long wavy-edged leaves that meet in the center of the stem.

Habitat. Swamp Milkweed prefers moist open areas and is typically found near the edges of ponds, lakes, open ditches, and low areas, ranging across Canada and south to Florida, Utah, and New Mexico. Both species are widespread across Virginia, Clasping Milkweed ranging from New Hampshire to Minnesota and south to Florida, Nebraska, and Texas.

Comments. Swamp Milkweed is one of the best attractors of the Monarch butterfly, which sips nectar from the flowers and lays its eggs on the plants. The leaves then provide a ready food source for the caterpillars. Although American colonists used Swamp Milkweed for asthma, rheumatism, and worms and as a heart tonic, the plant is potentially toxic. The genus name is from the Greek god of medicine, Asklepios.

Blooms July–September.

Left: Jan Newton   Right: Louise Menges

Common Milkweed

Asclepias syriaca   APOCYNACEAE Dogbane Family

Description. The coarse, unbranched stems of Common Milkweed grow to 3 feet tall. Leaves are on short petioles, thick, oval, gray-green, and minutely soft-hairy underneath. Both the central stem and leaves secrete a milky latex when torn. Pink to dark-purple flowers are heavily fragrant and occur in terminal and lateral clusters. The mature seedpods bear soft prickles and contain many flat seeds, dispersed airborne on a tuft of long hairs. White Milkweed (A. variegata) has white flowers, and its leaves are on slender petioles.

Habitat. Growing in every county in Virginia, Common Milkweed is found in fields, meadows, open woods, and roadsides over most of the eastern and central U.S. and Canada. While preferring full sun, it can tolerate a variety of situations, including partial sun and clay or sandy soil. White Milkweed occurs in upland woods and thickets across Virginia and from Ontario to Florida and Texas.

Comments. The caterpillars of the Monarch butterfly feed on the foliage, acquiring the toxic compounds in the leaves which protect them from predators. Deer avoid the plant because the leaves are bitter and poisonous. Native Americans found many uses for Common Milkweed, using the fiber for sewing thread, bowstrings, and fish lines.

Blooms June–August.

Field Thistle

Bull Thistle

Yellow Thistle

Left and right: Helen Hamilton   Center: Phillip Merritt

Field Thistle

NATIVE

Cirsium discolor   ASTERACEAE Aster Family

Description. A biennial, Field Thistle grows 3 to 7 feet tall in the second year, producing pink flower heads on erect stems. Slender golden spines project from the bracts on the swollen base of the flower head. The alternate leaves are lobed and spiny, green on the upper surface but powdery white below. The introduced Bull Thistle (*C. vulgare*, center) is very similar, but the bracts under the flower heads have thick coarse spines and the leaves are green on both sides. Stems are winged by the leaf bases. The leaves of the native Yellow Thistle (*C. horridulum*, right) are broad, lobed and very spiny, and narrow spiny-toothed leafy bracts surround the base of the yellow, sometimes red-purple, flower head.

Habitat. Field Thistle grows in roadsides and fields in every county in Virginia and throughout the eastern and central U.S. and Canada. Native to Eurasia, Bull Thistle is widely established in North America. Yellow Thistle occurs only in a few coastal counties in Virginia and in the eastern coastal states.

Comments. The American Goldfinch eats the seeds and lines its nests with thistledown, tufts of hair on the seeds. Bumblebees and butterflies visit the flowers for nectar and pollen. The caterpillars of the Painted Lady butterfly feed on the foliage.

Blooms August–November.

140

Coastal Joe Pye Weed NATIVE

Eutrochium dubium   ASTERACEAE Aster Family

Description. Tall, majestic perennials, the Joe Pye Weeds are real bee and butterfly magnets. Blooming from late summer until frost, they range from 3 to 10 feet tall, with dense, fluffy pinkish heads of disk flowers only (no ray flowers). Once included in *Eupatorium*, these species with leaves in whorls of 3 to 7 and pink to purple flowers are now separated into the genus *Eutrochium*. The leaves of Coastal Joe Pye Weed are 3-nerved from the base, abruptly contracted to the petiole, and strongly resin-dotted beneath. Two other Joe Pyes common in eastern Virginia have feather-veined leaves, only weakly or not resin-dotted. Hollow Joe Pye Weed *(E. fistulosum)* has hollow stems that are purple with a whitish bloom on the surface. The stem of Purple Joe Pye Weed *(E. purpureum)* is solid and greenish, except at the nodes.

Habitat. Coastal Joe Pye Weed prefers wet forests, meadows, and clearings in acid soil. The range is near the coast from Nova Scotia to South Carolina, including the eastern counties of Virginia.

Comments. Joe Pye, a legendary Native American, walked the streets of Boston selling an elixir of this plant to induce profuse sweating, which broke the fever of typhus.

Blooms July–October.

141

Saltmarsh Fleabane

Stinking Fleabane

Saltmarsh Fleabane

NATIVE

Pluchea odorata

ASTERACEAE Aster Family

Description. The purple-pink flowers of Saltmarsh Fleabane form small pubescent heads in a flattish cluster at the ends of stems and branches. The plant is 3 feet or more tall, its ovate to lance-shaped leaves often toothed. When bruised, the leaves emit a strong odor. A similar species, Camphorweed *(P. camphorata)*, of fresh rather than saline habitats, has thinner, often more serrate leaves and a rounded cluster of flower heads, these often with granular resin globules but nearly hairless. In both species the leaves are borne on short petioles or taper to the base. The leaves of Stinking Fleabane (*P. foetida*, right) are broad-based, clasping the shorter stem, and the flowers are creamy white.

Habitat. Saltmarsh Fleabane requires wet soil mainly in salty or brackish habitats and is found in Virginia in the coastal counties only. The species grows from Massachusetts to Florida and Texas, chiefly near the coast, locally in the Midwest and to tropical America. Camphorweed occurs in the southern counties of Virginia, while Stinking Fleabane is found in only a few southern Coastal Plain counties.

Comments. The genus was dedicated to the Abbé Noël-Antoine Pluche, French naturalist (1688–1761).

Blooms August–October.

142

Helen Hamilton

Deptford Pink

Dianthus armeria   CARYOPHYLLACEAE Pink Family

Description. Deep-pink flowers, ½ inch across, are arranged in flat-topped clusters. The flowers have 5 petals with jagged edges and tiny white spots. Erect leaf-like bracts below the flowers are lance-shaped. The stiff stems are up to 2 feet tall, with many basal leaves and 5 to 10 pairs of stem leaves. The leaves are grasslike, mostly less than ¼ inch wide.

Habitat. Deptford Pink is commonly found in dry fields and roadsides. A native of Europe, this annual or biennial weed is now established from Quebec and Ontario to British Columbia and south to Florida and Arkansas. The plant grows in every county in Virginia. A related perennial species, also introduced, Sweet William *(D. barbatus)* and its cultivars, are popular plants for local gardens.

Comments. The common name of the family probably refers to the notched, i.e., "pinked" petals of many species. The genus name *Dianthus* is derived from Greek *dios*, meaning "divine," and *anthos*, "flower"—this was the divine flower, or the flower of Zeus. The common name refers to Deptford, England (now part of London), where the flower was once abundant.

Blooms May–September.

Phillip Merritt

Soapwort

Saponaria officinalis   CARYOPHYLLACEAE Pink Family

Description. Easily recognized with its dense phlox-like cluster of flowers, Soapwort grows 1 to 3 feet tall on smooth stems swollen at the nodes. Each of the 5 petals has a slender lower portion (claw) hidden in the long tubular calyx. The upper portions expand into pink or white blades notched at the tips, forming a flower an inch wide. In pairs on the stem, the oval leaves have 2 to 5 prominent ribs. This perennial spreads by underground stems to form large colonies.

Habitat. Native to the Old World, Soapwort has been cultivated and is now established as a weed of roadsides, waste places, and railways throughout most of temperate North America. It occurs in every county in Virginia.

Comments. The genus name comes from Latin *sapo*, meaning "soap." *Officinalis* means "medicinal." The plant contains soap-like substances (saponins); when the roots are crushed and added to water, the soapy lather can be used to wash clothes. The plant has been used by Native Americans and Europeans medicinally, but the saponins can be poisonous in large quantity. The other common name, Bouncing Bet, is an old expression for a washerwoman.

Blooms May–October.

144

Marsh Dewflower INTRODUCED INVASIVE

Murdannia keisak   COMMELINACEAE Spiderwort Family

Description. Often growing immersed in water, the succulent stems of Marsh Dewflower are weak, often prostrate and rooting at the nodes, and can be more than 30 inches long. The alternate leaves arise from a basal sheath, the blade narrowly lance-shaped and up to 2½ inches long. In late summer small 3-petaled white or pink to bluish-purple flowers occur singly or in small clusters at the tops of stems and in the leaf axils. A very prolific annual, it produces thousands of very small seeds and also spreads vegetatively.

Habitat. This plant has been associated with rice culture in east Asia and may have been accidentally introduced to this country along with rice imported for production. Found in freshwater marshes, in wet roadside ditches, and along the edges of ponds and streams, Marsh Dewflower occurs in all the counties of the Coastal Plain. A terribly invasive species, it is increasing in the Piedmont and Ridge and Valley provinces of Virginia, and ranges from Maryland to Florida and Mississippi inland to Kentucky and Arkansas.

Comments. This highly aggressive plant crowds out native species by forming a solid mat of vegetation. The seeds are relished by waterfowl, which aid in their dispersal.

Blooms September–October.

Hedge Bindweed

NATIVE/INTRODUCED

Calystegia sepium   CONVOLVULACEAE Morning Glory Family

Description. This smooth twining vine has funnel-shaped flowers 2 inches or more wide and pinkish with white stripes, formed by 5 petals fused together. The two large pale-green bracts at the base of the flower are distinctive. Leaves are triangular in outline with basal lobes pointed outwards. A related introduced species, Field Bindweed *(Convolvulus arvensis),* has smaller flowers an inch or less wide and lacking the large bracts. Field Bindweed is a noxious weed in many areas of temperate North America and Eurasia, difficult to eradicate because of the deep root.

Habitat. Hedge Bindweed grows in thickets, on shores, and on disturbed sites in temperate regions of North America and Eurasia, and in every county in Virginia. Both native and introduced forms are present in this country.

Comments. Once included in the genus *Ipomoea,* Hedge Bindweed differs from other members of the Morning Glory Family in having two elongate stigmas rather than one 2- to 3-lobed stigma. Further, Hedge Bindweed is a native perennial, while several widespread *Ipomoea* species are introduced annuals. The species name *sepium* is the Latin term for "hedge." This plant has been used historically as a purgative.

Blooms May–September.

146

Left: Helen Hamilton   Right: Seig Kopinitz

Panicled Tick-trefoil

Desmodium paniculatum

NATIVE

FABACEAE Pea Family

Description. These are slender plants with small rosy-pink flowers in loose clusters. The flowers have the typical pea-like structure of an upright petal and 2 lateral wings enclosing a central keel. At the base of the upper petal (the banner) there are 2 tiny patches of yellow. The 3 leaflets, relatively slender and of variable width, appear horizontal to the ground. The seedpods (loments) have 3 to 5 joints and are covered with tiny hooked hairs by which they adhere to clothing. Twelve species of *Desmodium* occur in the Coastal Plain of Virginia, differentiated by the shape of the leaflets, the number of joints in the loments, and the flower color.

Habitat. Panicled Tick-trefoil grows in dry woods, woodland edges, thickets, and partially shaded roadside embankments. This wildflower is a pioneer species that appears on disturbed ground. The plant is widespread across Virginia and ranges from southern Maine to southern Ontario, Michigan, and Nebraska south to Florida and Texas.

Comments. Also known as Sticktights and Beggar's-ticks, the sticky seedpods cling to the fur of animals and the clothing of humans, thus carried to new locations.

Blooms June–September.

147

Perennial
Sand Bean

Annual
Sand Bean

Helen Hamilton

Perennial Sand Bean

NATIVE

Strophostyles umbellata

FABACEAE Pea Family

Description. This low herbaceous perennial has slender branching and trailing stems. Leaflets are in threes, oblong and smooth. Several pink (fading to yellow) flowers appear at the ends of stalks that extend beyond the leaves. As in the flowers of many other species of the Pea Family, the 5 petals consist of an upper banner, 2 lateral wing petals, and 2 lower petals united into a boat-like keel. Bean-like seedpods are 2 inches or more long. The leaflets of Annual Sand Bean (*S. helvola*, right) are usually 3-lobed, the terminal one an inch or more wide.

Habitat. Preferring sandy soils, these plants grow in fields, thin woods, and thickets in the eastern and Piedmont counties of Virginia. Annual Sand Bean is a pioneer plant frequently found colonizing open sites in either moist or dry conditions, often on cinders. Perennial Sand Bean ranges from southern New York to Florida and Texas north in the interior to Indiana and Oklahoma. Annual Sand Bean occurs north to Quebec, Minnesota, and South Dakota.

Comments. Native Americans have used these plants for food and medicinally. Northern Bobwhite and Wild Turkeys are among the birds that feed on the seeds. The genus name, from Greek, refers to the curved style.

Blooms June–September.

Left: Phillip Merritt   Right: Seig Kopinitz

Goat's Rue

Tephrosia virginiana   FABACEAE Pea Family

Description. This distinctive perennial is marked by showy, bicolored, typical pea-like flowers, the upper petal pale yellow, the others pink or pale purple. Less than 1 inch long, the flowers are crowded into clusters at the top of a 1- to 2-foot hairy stem. The pinnately compound leaves are divided into 7 to 12 pairs of oblong leaflets plus one leaflet at the tip. The fruit is a narrow, whitish hairy pod up to 2 inches long. Most of the plant may be covered in long, soft, even silky hair.

Habitat. Goat's Rue is widespread in Virginia, growing in dry, sandy woods and clearings. The range is from New Hampshire to Florida west to southeast Minnesota, Kansas, and Texas.

Comments. The name *Tephrosia* originated from Greek *tephros* meaning "ash-colored" or "hoary." This plant has traditionally been used to treat ailments such as tuberculosis, rheumatism, and bladder troubles and has been studied in cancer research.

The tough, slender, woody roots contain nitrogen-fixing bacteria valuable for soil fertility, but they are highly poisonous due to the presence of rotenone. Native Americans used the crushed roots to kill fish and made a tea to pour on undesirable insects.

Blooms May–June.

Helen Hamilton

Rabbitfoot Clover

INTRODUCED

Trifolium arvense

FABACEAE Pea Family

Description. With soft, fuzzy flowers resembling a miniature rabbit's foot, this plant is well named and unmistakable. The oblong, grayish spikes of flowers are so dense and furry that the actual tiny pink (or white) flowers are largely concealed. The 3 leaflets of the compound leaf are narrow and silky-hairy. This branching annual plant, softly hairy throughout, grows up to 2 feet tall.

Habitat. Introduced from Europe, Rabbitfoot Clover is now common along roadsides and in waste places. It grows in dry sandy soils, typically found at the edge of fields, in wastelands, on sand dunes, and invades vineyards and orchards when they are not irrigated. Found in nearly every county in Virginia, the plant ranges throughout much of the U.S. and southern Canada.

Comments. The species name *arvense* means "of cultivated fields." Unlike other clovers, this one is useless as fodder. The plant has been reported to produce dermatitis and photosensitization in domestic animals, and if mature heads are eaten by livestock, mechanical intestinal irritation may result. However, all the clovers are rich in nitrogen and nourish adjacent plants to a dark green.

Blooms April–August.

Louise Menges

Red Clover

Trifolium pratense   FABACEAE Pea Family

Description. Red Clover is a short-lived perennial with attractive pink to purplish-pink rounded flower heads in a cluster that may be over an inch long. As in most members of the Pea Family, the 5 petals consist of an upper banner, 2 wings, and 2 lower petals joined as a keel. The leaves are alternate on the stem and divided into 3 leaflets, each usually with a pale chevron near the middle. The plant grows to 2 feet tall; its lower leaves have long hairy petioles, while those of the upper leaves are shorter.

Habitat. Native to Europe, Red Clover is widespread in Virginia, growing in open fields, meadows, and lawns. The plant has become established as a weed along roadsides and in waste places throughout much of North America.

Comments. Red Clover is one of the world's most important hay and pasture plants. Nectar is available to bumblebees with their long tongues, but the flowers are too large for honeybees. Red Clover has been used by Native Americans for fever, whooping cough, as a "blood medicine," and for cancer, and, with Timothy *(Phleum pratense)*, for cattle feed. However, Red Clover is also reported to cause serious internal symptoms and abortion in cattle.

Blooms April–September.

Left: Helen Hamilton   Right: Phillip Merritt

Spring Vetch

Vicia sativa   FABACEAE Pea Family

Description. Spring Vetch is a slender annual legume to 3 feet, often climbing. Compound leaves ending in tendrils bear 6 to 16 leaflets. Nearly stalkless pea-like pink-purple flowers, mostly in pairs, arise in the upper axils. Hairy Vetch *(V. villosa)*, with 10 to 20 leaflets, has long flowering stalks (peduncles) bearing elongate, 1-sided clusters of 10 to 40 violet flowers.

Habitat. Both species are native to Europe, introduced in fields, on roadsides, and in waste places through most of the U.S. and southern Canada. Growing in nearly every county in Virginia, these vetches can be aggressive weeds.

Comments. *Vicia* is the classical Latin name from a verb meaning "to bind," referring to the clasping tendrils. Vetches are able to fix atmospheric nitrogen; Hairy Vetch is used by organic growers as a winter cover crop and is often planted with tomatoes. In the spring the vetch is cut to the ground and the tomato seedlings are planted in holes dug through the matted residue. The vetch foliage provides nitrogen and instant mulch that preserves moisture and retards weeds.

Blooms April–June.

Rose Pink

Marsh Pink

Rose Pink

NATIVE

Sabatia angularis   GENTIANACEAE Gentian Family

Description. Rose Pink is well named for its 1-inch deep-pink flowers of 5 petal-like lobes with a yellow or greenish center. This robust biennial grows to 2 feet tall and commonly has many upper branches growing opposite with sharp-angled wings. Leaves are opposite, entire, and rounded at the base, often clasping the stem, ½ to 1½ inches wide. The showy annual Marsh Pink (*S. stellaris*, right) has narrow leaves less than ½ inch wide and the upper branches alternate. White blossoms occasionally appear in either species.

Habitat. Growing in many habitats, Rose Pink is widespread across Virginia. Its range is from Connecticut to southern Michigan and Kansas and south to Florida and Texas. Marsh Pink is common on the Coastal Plain, growing in full sun in saline or brackish marshes, in wet sand, and at pond margins.

Comments. The genus name honors Liberato Sabbati, an 18th-century surgeon and curator of the Rome botanic garden. The inhabitants of Plymouth, Massachusetts, were convinced that the Pilgrims of 1620 named the plant *Sabatia* after the Sabbath, the holy day on which they first saw the flower, and that "strong objections are made if any other flowers are irreverently mingled with it in church decorations."

Blooms July–September.

153

Teta Kain

Stork's Bill

INTRODUCED

Erodium cicutarium   GERANIACEAE Geranium Family

Description. Stork's Bill is well named for its fruit, which forms a projection up to an inch long—the "bill" of the stork. The bright rose-purple flowers are small (¼ inch across) on very short pedicels in long-talked clusters among deeply cut and pinnately divided leaves; related geraniums have palmately divided leaves. At maturity the fruit splits into 5 spirally twisted segments. This is a winter annual or biennial, producing rosettes of overwintering leaves. While the stems are often spread flat on the soil in a rosette, they can grow to one foot tall.

Habitat. Growing in waste places, roadsides, and cultivated fields, Stork's Bill is found in the coastal counties and some central and mountainous areas. A native of the Mediterranean region, it is now established as a common weed throughout most of the U.S.

Comments. Stork's Bill was named from Greek *erodios,* "a heron," from the long beak of its fruit. Native American tribes used the plant for infections, wildcat bites, typhoid fever, sores, and stomachaches. Early leaves were cooked as greens; roots were chewed by children, sometimes as gum. This is a good grazing plant for horses, cows, sheep, and rabbits.

Blooms March–June.

Carolina Geranium

Dovefoot Geranium

Carolina Geranium

NATIVE

Geranium carolinianum   GERANIACEAE Geranium Family

Description. This winter annual or biennial grows 6 to 20 inches tall with deeply cut leaves. Pale pink flowers are crowded in compact clusters. Each flower develops a long beak-shaped fruit of peculiar structure: the swollen base of the fruit splits at maturity into 5 units, each containing a single black seed and attached to a strip of beak tissue. These strips break free and curl upward, carrying the ripe seeds at their tips. The similar Cut-leaf Geranium *(G. dissectum)*, a weed from Europe, has deeper pink flowers and fruit with shorter, minutely gland-tipped hairs. A native of Europe and western Asia, Dovefoot Geranium *(G. molle,* right) has a more rounded leaf with short blunt lobes. The flowers are deep red-purple, about ½ inch across, with deeply notched petals.

Habitat. These weedy Geraniums grow in dry, barren, or sandy soil, fields, on roadsides, and in waste places. Found throughout Virginia, their range extends through the U.S. and southern Canada.

Comments. The genus derives from Greek *geranos,* "a crane," the fruit resembling the bill of a crane. These plants have been used medicinally and are high in tannins, with antibacterial, antiviral, and astringent properties.

Blooms March–June.

Purple Deadnettle

Henbit Deadnettle

Purple Deadnettle

INTRODUCED

Lamium purpureum   LAMIACEAE Mint Family

Description. Purple Deadnettle is a low-growing annual weed. Two-lipped flowers are red-purple, and the leaves around the flowers are often purplish. The heart-shaped, stalked leaves are opposite each other on the stem. This plant is easily mistaken for Henbit Deadnettle (*L. amplexicaule*, right), also introduced, since the flower structure is similar and the two plants often grow in the same habitat. These two plants can be distinguished by the attachment of the leaves to the stem—either with stalks in Purple Deadnettle or attached directly (sessile and clasping) in Henbit Deadnettle.

Habitat. These are common weeds of waste places, roadsides, fields, and woods. They are native to Eurasia and now established throughout much of the U.S. Both species are long-blooming and can be seen along pathways, near dwellings, and in lawns in every county in Virginia.

Comments. In early spring dense populations of these plants will color pastures and fields with bright purple. Young plants have edible tops and leaves, good in salads or cooked as a spring vegetable. Though superficially similar to a nettle in appearance, they are not closely related and do not sting, hence the name "deadnettle."

Blooms March–October.

Scarlet Beebalm

Spotted Beebalm

Wild Bergamot

Spotted Beebalm

NATIVE

Monarda punctata   LAMIACEAE Mint Family

Description. Spotted Beebalm grows to 3 feet with finely hairy, squarish stems. The opposite, narrowly oblong leaves are pointed at both ends with a few small teeth. Flowers are strongly 2-lipped, yellowish with purple spots, in dense whorls along the stem; lavender to white leaf-like bracts surround the flowers. Two other species bear flowers only in a terminal head at the tips of the stems. Scarlet Beebalm or Oswego-tea (*M. didyma,* upper right) produces stunning true red flowers. The dense heads of pink to lavender flowers of Wild Bergamot (*M. fistulosa,* lower right) look like ragged pompons.

Habitat. This species grows in old fields and dry, sandy soils in eastern and central counties in Virginia. The range is from New Jersey to Florida and Texas, chiefly on the Coastal Plain. Scarlet Beebalm is native to a few counties in western Virginia; Wild Bergamot grows in the mountain region and in a few Piedmont and coastal counties.

Comments. Linnaeus named the genus in honor of Spanish physician and botanist Nicolas Monardes (1493–1588), author of the book *Joyful Newes out of the Newe Founde Worlde.* The aromatic leaves of *Monarda* species have been used to make mint tea, the oil to treat respiratory ailments.

Blooms July–September.

Swamp Loosestrife

Purple Loosestrife

Left: Teta Kain   Right: Phillip Merritt

Swamp Loosestrife   NATIVE

Decodon verticillatus   LYTHRACEAE Loosestrife Family

Description. This is a sprawling perennial with long, arching stems that often submerge and root at their tips. Lance-shaped leaves on short petioles are opposite or in whorls of 3 or 4 on the stem. Clustering in the leaf axils, pink to purple flowers are bell-shaped with 5 petals, 4 to 5 long, protruding stamens, and 4 to 5 short ones. Also known as Water Willow, this species is not one of the true willows, which are shrubs or trees that do not produce pink flowers. Purple Loosestrife (*Lythrum salicaria*, right, see also page 199) is an extremely invasive introduced weed with 6-petaled flowers with mostly 12 stamens and sessile leaves.

Habitat. Swamp Loosestrife grows in Virginia only in the coastal counties, in standing water of marshes or swamps or in tidal freshwater wetlands. The species ranges from Nova Scotia and Minnesota and south to Florida and Louisiana. Native to Eurasia, Purple Loosestrife is an extremely noxious weed, rapidly replacing native vegetation in freshwater wetlands.

Comments. The genus name *Decodon* comes from Greek *deca,* "ten," and *odous,* "tooth," referring to the jagged appearance of the flower parts; *verticillatus,* "whorled," describes the leaf arrangement.

Blooms July–September.

158

Seashore Mallow

Kosteletzkya pentacarpos   MALVACEAE Mallow Family

Description. This coarse, hairy perennial resembles members of the genus *Hibiscus*, but the flowers are much smaller and a deep pink. No more than 3 inches across, they are in terminal, often leafy, clusters that close at night. As in other members of the Mallow Family, the stamens are fused into a yellow central column. Gray-green hairy leaves are variable in shape, the lower leaves usually with 3 to 5 lobes and smaller upper leaves lanceolate to triangular. Angular, much-branched stems are 1 to 3 feet tall.

Habitat. Growing in full sun in brackish marshes, swamps, and shores, Seashore Mallow occurs only in the Coastal Plain in Virginia. Moderately salt tolerant, the plant prefers sand and soils with high acidity but will tolerate clay habitats. This species ranges from Long Island to Florida and Texas and to the West Indies.

Comments. Seashore Mallow attracts butterflies and hummingbirds. The genus was named for Vincenz Kostelezky (1801–1887), a Bohemian botanist.

Blooms July–October.

Pale Meadow Beauty NATIVE

Rhexia mariana   MELASTOMATACEAE Melastome Family

Description. The flowers of meadow beauties are unmistakable—4 large purplish to pale rose to white petals surround the long, upwardly curving anthers hanging downward. The leaves on the midstem are opposite, lance-shaped to elliptical, and somewhat toothed. Very characteristic of the family, rather than a single prominent midrib, leaves possess 3 more or less equally developed large veins. Growing more than 2 feet tall, the stems are softly hairy with two narrow flattish sides and two broader ones. The petals of Virginia Meadow Beauty *(R. virginica)* are deep purple to magenta, and the stem has 4 subequal sides, and is conspicuously winged.

Habitat. This plant is common in sandy bogs, marsh edges, and roadside ditches of the Coastal Plain, growing in the eastern and central counties of Virginia. The range is from Massachusetts to Florida west to southern Indiana and Texas.

Comments. The family name comes from Greek *melas,* "black," and *stoma,* "mouth," the mouth being stained black by the fruit of some species. The Melastome Family, one of the largest families of the flowering plants, is mostly tropical, principally of South America. Of 188 genera with nearly 5,000 species, there is only one other genus, *Tetrazygia,* with a species native to the U.S.—Florida Clover Ash *(T. bicolor).*

 Blooms May–October.

Pink
Lady's-slipper

Yellow
Lady's-slipper

Left: Teta Kain   Right: Ian Newton

Pink Lady's-slipper

Cypripedium acaule   ORCHIDACEAE Orchid Family

Description. No flower is more recognizable than the Pink Lady's-slipper, with a distinctive inflated slipper-like lip petal, veined with red and with a crease down the front. This is our only lady's-slipper without stem leaves; at the base of the flower stem is a pair of wide, ribbed, oval 8-inch leaves. Yellow Lady's-slipper (*C. parviflorum* var. *pubescens*, right) has a bright-yellow lip and leaves closely spaced alternately up the stem.

Habitat. These orchids are found in acid soil, from swamps and bogs to dry woods and sand dunes. They do poorly in deep shade and are usually found in old forests with a broken canopy or in young forests regenerating after logging or fire. Pink Lady's-slipper is native to every county in Virginia and in most areas of the eastern and central U.S. and Canada. Yellow Lady's-slipper grows in only a few of Virginia's coastal counties, preferring limy soils.

Comments. The Lady's-slippers are among the showiest of all temperate-zone orchids, but family members are extravagantly diverse in form and size in the tropics. With some 800 genera and perhaps 35,000 species, orchids compete with the asters as the largest family of flowering plants.

Blooms April–May.

161

Felice Bond

Showy Orchid

Galearis spectabilis ORCHIDACEAE Orchid Family

Description. These small orchids are striking, with a stalk of 2 to 15 pink to pale purple and white flowers in the axils of conspicuous bracts. The sepals and petals form an arching hood, while the lower petal is white and broad with ruffled edges. The base of the lip is prolonged into an interesting tubular spur behind the flower. The two large, glossy-green leaves are paired at the base of the plant. Characteristic of the Orchid Family in general, the fruit is a capsule with an immense number of minute seeds.

Habitat. Showy Orchid requires moderate moisture in rich, sometimes limy soil. Widespread across Virginia, the plant ranges from New Brunswick to Minnesota and Nebraska and south to Georgia and Arkansas.

Comments. The genus name *Galearis* is derived from Latin *galea*, meaning "helmet," referring to the two pink to purple upper petals and the sepals, which form a hood over the flower. *Spectabilis* is from Latin for "remarkable, showy." This species has traditionally been placed in the genus *Orchis* for which the Orchid Family as a whole is named. *Orchis*, Greek for "testicle," is the ancient name referring to the swollen, ball-shaped tubers of some species. Orchids have been widely regarded as aphrodisiacs.

Blooms April–May.

162

Summer Phlox

NATIVE

Phlox paniculata   POLEMONIACEAE Phlox Family

Description. The pyramidal cluster of bright magenta-pink flowers on stout, erect, smooth 1- to 3-foot stems defines Summer Phlox. Each flower has 5 petals with spreading lobes tightly united below into a tube. Leaves are opposite and broadly lance-shaped with bristly margins and prominent side veins.

Habitat. Summer Phlox prefers moist, acid, rich soil in sun or shade. It tolerates seasonal flooding and blooms vigorously during the hottest part of the summer; this perennial grows on streambanks, on roadsides, in rich open woods, and in thickets. In Virginia, it is found in coastal and northern counties and scattered in the mountainous regions. Common in the eastern and central U.S., the plant ranges from southern New York to northern Georgia west to Illinois, Missouri, and Arkansas, and has escaped from cultivation elsewhere.

Comments. Summer Phlox has been widely used as a medicinal herb; the leaf extract serves as a laxative and for treating boils. Butterflies and hummingbirds sip nectar from the flowers. Summer Phlox is widely cultivated and many cultivars are available in colors ranging from white to violet-blue.

Blooms July–August.

Arrowleaf Tearthumb

Halberd-leaf Tearthumb

Helen Hamilton

Arrowleaf Tearthumb

NATIVE

Persicaria sagittata   POLYGONACEAE Smartweed Family

Description. These freely branched annuals are erect when young, then recumbent on other plants. They are well named, as the 4-angled stem will tear a thumb on its backward-pointing barbs. Smooth leaves with arrow-shaped bases are 1 to 4 inches long on 1-inch petioles; small white or pink flowers usually cluster at the end of branches. Halberd-leaf Tearthumb (*P. arifolia,* right) is similar, with somewhat hairy, triangle-shaped leaves on longer petioles.

Habitat. Both species grow in wet ground, often in brackish habitats, and are widespread across Virginia. Arrowleaf Tearthumb ranges from Newfoundland and Quebec to Saskatchewan and south to Georgia and Texas. Halberd-leaf Tearthumb ranges from New Brunswick to Minnesota and south to Georgia and Missouri.

Comments. These plants were formerly in the genus *Polygonum. Persicaria* refers to the resemblance of the leaves of some species to those of the Persian apple tree, or peach. The species name *sagittata* comes from the Latin word for "arrowhead," and *arifolia* describes the shape of the leaves, similar to those of Arrow Arum (*Peltandra virginica,* page 214).

Blooms May–December.

Rough Buttonweed

Rough Buttonweed

Virginia Buttonweed

Left and bottom right: Helen Hamilton   Top right: Phillip Merritt

Rough Buttonweed

NATIVE

Diodia teres

RUBIACEAE Madder Family

Description. This little plant is not particularly showy and is easily overlooked. Buttonweed is a prostrate, spreading annual with somewhat hairy round stems. Leaves are opposite, firm and narrow, feeling rough to the touch; at the base of the leaves are distinctive long bristles. The flower is funnel-shaped, ¼ inch wide, pale purple to white. The fruit looks like a swollen button and is green and shiny, eventually turning brown. Virginia Buttonweed (*D. virginiana*, lower right) differs in its larger, usually pure-white petal lobes abruptly expanding from a narrow tube, slender styles, and 2-lobed calyx. Rough Buttonweed has knobby undivided styles and 4 calyx lobes.

Habitat. Rough Buttonweed prefers full sun, dry conditions, and poor soil of sand, gravel, or compacted clay, occurring in almost every county in Virginia. The plant is drought tolerant, growing in dry sandy soil even where eroded and depleted in nutrients. It ranges along the East and Gulf coasts from southern New England to Texas.

Comments. Other common names for Rough Buttonweed are Poorjoe and Poverty Weed, reflecting this plant's tolerance of poor soil. Virginia Buttonweed is an annual or perennial of wet soil.

Blooms June–November.

165

Fog Fruit

NATIVE

Phyla lanceolata   VERBENACEAE Verbena Family

Description. Small but distinctive flower heads appear at the end of long stems arising from the leaf axils; the tightly packed globes of flowers soon elongate into cylinders more than an inch long. Individual flowers are less than ¼ inch across and tubular, with 4 irregular lobes; they vary from pink or bluish white to white with a yellow eye. They are surrounded by darker leaf-like scales (bracts). This perennial has square, creeping stems that root freely. Leaves are opposite on the stem, lance-shaped to elliptic, tapering, and toothed.

Habitat. Fogfruit grows in bottomlands, on shores of creeks and lakes, and in marshes in many of the Coastal Plain counties in Virginia. The plant ranges from Ontario to Minnesota and South Dakota and south to Florida and Mexico.

Comments. The genus name is from Greek *phyle*, meaning "tribe," probably from the flowers tightly clustered in heads; *lanceolata* refers to the lance-shaped leaves. The common name may be related to their usual habitat in wet and frequently foggy areas; the plant is also known as Frog Fruit.

Blooms June–November.

Helen Hamilton

Chicory INTRODUCED

Cichorium intybus ASTERACEAE Aster Family

Description. Sky-blue flower heads cover the roadsides in late summer and early fall. This perennial can grow up to 4 feet tall from a long taproot, the long flowering branches producing 1 to 3 flower heads in the angles of the upper leaves. When the days are hot, the flowers open only in the morning but remain expanded longer with cooler weather. Leaves are numerous around the base, cut and lobed much as in Dandelion, but much smaller along the branched stems. When broken, the stems exude a milky latex.

Habitat. Chicory grows in roadsides, fields and waste places all over Virginia. A native of Europe, the plant is now a cosmopolitan weed. Very easy to grow, the plants tolerate rocks or other debris in the soil, thriving best along roadsides.

Comments. The Cherokee used an infusion of root as a tonic for nerves and the Iroquois applied a decoction of roots to fever sores. Chicory is an edible plant; the blanched hearts serve as a vegetable, the leaves are added to salads, and roots are used in seasoning soups, sauces and gravies. The root of the European Root-chicory (*C. intybus* var. *sativum*) is baked, ground, and used as a coffee substitute.

Blooms May–November.

167

Helen Hamilton

Hairy Elephant's Foot

Elephantopus tomentosus   ASTERACEAE   Aster Family

Description. The common name of this branching perennial, growing to 2 feet tall, refers to the wide oval leaves, velvety to the touch and clustering in a basal rosette. Two other species of this interesting plant can be found in our area. Smooth Elephant's Foot *(E. nudatus)* is very similar, but the leaves are narrower and only sparsely pubescent except for stiff, straight hairs along the veins underneath. The leaves of the third local species, Carolina Elephant's Foot *(E. carolinianus)*, are mostly on the stem, not at the base. The flowering stems of all 3 plants have small leaf-like bracts at the junction of the stem and flower stalk. Flower heads are bluish purple, surrounded by small, triangular bracts.

Habitat. Hairy Elephant's Foot grows in open, sandy woods on the Coastal Plain from southeast Virginia to Florida, Texas, and Mexico and north to the interior of Kentucky. Carolina Elephant's Foot is widespread across Virginia, while Hairy and Smooth Elephant's Foot are concentrated in the central and eastern counties.

Comments. The scientific name of these plants is composed of Greek *elephas,* "elephant," and *pous,* "foot." Linnaeus used this genus name for a species found in India.

Blooms August–November.

Phillip Merritt

Perennial Saltmarsh Aster

NATIVE

Symphyotrichum tenuifolium
(Aster tenuifolius)

ASTERACEAE Aster Family

Description. This is an erect to sprawling plant with narrow fleshy leaves few and far apart and few to many flower heads. Growing at the tips of branches, the flowers have 15 to 25 pale blue to pinkish rays ¾ inch or so long. Although this perennial aster has few flowers, it forms conspicuous masses in brackish tidal marshes, from which all other large-flowered species are absent. The Annual Saltmarsh Aster *(S. subulatum)* may have few or numerous small heads but, with rays ⅛ inch or less, they are much less conspicuous.

Habitat. This plant grows in salt marshes and shores from Massachusetts to Florida and Louisiana. In Virginia, both species are found only in the eastern counties, though the overall range of the annual species is much broader.

Comments. *Aster* is derived from the Greek word meaning "star," referring to the radiate heads of the flowers. The species name *tenuifolium* means "slender-leaved." The new genus name derives from Greek *symphy(o)* "coming together," and *trich(o)* "hair," possibly referring to the coherent anthers.

Blooms July–November.

Wild Comfrey

NATIVE

Cynoglossum virginianum   BORAGINACEAE Borage Family

Description. This rough, hairy perennial grows to 2 feet or more tall. The leaves at the base are large; the alternate stem leaves are smaller and clasp the hairy stem. The small, about ½-inch-wide flower looks like a Forget-me-not, but the large basal leaves and upright habit are not found in Forget-me-nots. The pale blue flowers have 5 lobes and grow in clusters at the end of a stalk; each flower produces 4 small nutlets covered with bristles that cling to fur and clothing.

Habitat. Widely distributed across Virginia, Wild Comfrey grows mostly in upland woods from Quebec to Minnesota west to British Columbia and south to Florida and Louisiana. A weedy Eurasian species, Hound's-tongue *(C. officinale)* with reddish-purple flowers is widespread in western Virginia.

Comments. The genus is named from Greek *cynos*, "of a dog," and *glossa,* "tongue," from the shape and texture of the leaves. Cherokee used the root tea for cancer, itching of genitals, and milky urine. The tea of this and other plants with clinging fruits was thought to improve memory, an application of the Doctrine of Signatures, the belief that the form of a plant or plant part reveals its curative properties. In more recent times the leaves were smoked like tobacco.

Blooms April–June.

Great Blue Lobelia

NATIVE

Lobelia siphilitica   CAMPANULACEAE Bellflower Family

Description. Flowers of the genus *Lobelia* all have 2 narrow lobes or "ears" above, with 3 wider lobes forming a lip below. The 1-inch-long violet-blue flowers of Great Blue Lobelia are striped with white on the 3 lower lobes. Leaves are alternate on the stem, finely toothed and pointed. The plant grows 1 to 3 feet high, with the flowers arranged in an elongate terminal cluster on a stiff, unbranched leafy stalk. The many-seeded capsule opens at the top.

Habitat. Great Blue Lobelia is easily grown in wet to moist fertile and loamy soil in partial sun; in full sun the soil must be consistently moist. Found in meadows, moist thickets, and swamps from Maine to Manitoba and Colorado and south to North Carolina and Texas, Great Blue Lobelia grows in most counties of Virginia.

Comments. Early medical writers thought Native Americans used the root primarily to treat syphilis, hence the species name *siphilitica*. While the plant is potentially poisonous, Native Americans used root tea for syphilis and leaf tea for a number of illnesses such as colds, worms, nosebleed, coughs and headaches.

Blooms July–October.

171

Helen Hamilton

European Corn-salad INTRODUCED

Valerianella locusta (V. olitoria) CAPRIFOLIACEAE Honeysuckle Family

Description. European Corn-salad is a low, distinctly forked plant with sprawling stems 4 to 12 inches tall. Not showy, the minute pale blue flowers are in small flat groups with leafy bracts beneath. The oblong leaves are sessile and opposite on the stem. The tiny fruit (nutlet) has a corky thickening on one side. The flowers of the native species, Beaked Corn-salad *(V. radiata)*, are white in color and the nutlet lacks the corky mass present on the European species.

Habitat. This small annual grows in moist open places, along roadsides, and in lawns and garden edges, often in disturbed areas. A native of Europe now widely established in the U.S., European Corn-salad can be found in most counties in Virginia. Beaked Corn-salad also occurs in most counties in Virginia, ranging to Ohio, southern Illinois, and Kansas and south to Florida and Texas.

Comments. Originally foraged by European peasants, European Corn-salad has many nutrients, including three times as much Vitamin C as lettuce. The leaves can be eaten in salads, preferably gathered before the blooms appear. Also known as Lamb's-lettuce, its common name probably arose because this weedy little salad plant often appeared growing wild in corn fields.

Blooms April–May.

Asiatic Dayflower INTRODUCED

Commelina communis COMMELINACEAE Spiderwort Family

Description. Asiatic Dayflower is a sprawling annual, growing
1 to 3 feet tall. The plant can root at the leaf nodes, producing new
plants vegetatively, and can form colonies that exclude other species of plants. The entire plant is almost succulent, with thick, watery
stems and long oval leaves clasping the stem. Each flower blooms in
the morning for a single day, hence the common name. The flowers
are distinctive, with two prominent earlike blue petals above and a
smaller whitish petal beneath. This imported weed differs from the
native Virginia Dayflower *(C. virginica)* by its small white (not blue)
lower petal and narrower leaves.

Habitat. Growing in roadsides, waste places, on moist or shaded ground
across the eastern and central U.S. and Canada, Asiatic Dayflower is
found in nearly every county in Virginia. A native of Asia, the plant was
introduced into this country and is now considered a garden weed.

Comments. The genus name *Commelina* recognizes two Dutch botanists, Johan and Caspar Commelin, who are represented by the two
large sky-blue petals; the third brother who made no scientific contri-
butions is memorialized by the insignificant third petal. The species
name *communis* refers to the "community" growth pattern.

Blooms May–October.

Wild Lupine   NATIVE

Lupinus perennis   FABACEAE Pea Family

Description. Wild Lupine is easily recognized as a member of the Pea Family, with its typical blue or violet flowers in an upright, elongate terminal cluster. The leaves are divided in a palm-like pattern into 7 to 10 lance-shaped leaflets up to 2 inches long. Hairy seedpods are produced that open forcefully, throwing the seeds some distance. Imported European species of lupine have larger flowers in various colors of red, yellow, orange, or white.

Habitat. Wild Lupine grows well in dry, sandy acidic soils and is often seen in dry, open woods and clearings. Reported from eastern and northwestern counties of Virginia, the plant ranges from southern Maine to Florida and west to Minnesota and Indiana.

Comments. The genus name is derived from Latin *lupus*, for "wolf," because the plant was once thought to deplete or "wolf" the mineral content of the soil. Actually, all members of the Pea (Legume) Family enhance soil fertility with bacterial nodules on their roots that fix atmospheric nitrogen into a usable form. The pea-like seeds contain a poisonous alkaloid and are not a substitute for peas, although some exotic species are edible. Bluebonnet *(L. texensis)* is the state flower of Texas.

Blooms April–May.

174

Lyre-leaved Sage

NATIVE

Salvia lyrata   LAMIACEAE Mint Family

Description. Lavender-blue flowers about 1 inch long in whorls of 3 to 10 surround the square stem to form a very interrupted spike-like cluster. The flowers have 2 lips, the lower longer than the upper. Lyre-leaved Sage is a fibrous-rooted perennial with a hairy stem growing 1 to 2 feet tall. The leaves are mostly at the base, usually deeply lobed ("lyre-shaped") and long-stalked, forming a rosette. Stem leaves are few and much smaller.

Habitat. This perennial grows in sandy, open woods and thickets in every county in Virginia. The range is from Connecticut to southern Ohio and Missouri and south to Florida and Texas.

Comments. The plant is also known as Cancerweed, since the leaves were once thought to be an external cure for cancer. The genus name comes from Latin *salvare*, meaning "to save or heal." Native Americans used the root in ointments for sores and whole-plant tea medicinally, and seeds of some species were ground into flour. The trumpet-shaped flowers are attractive to bees and butterflies. When a bee lands on the exposed lower lip, the 2 stamens are tipped, and the insect is dusted with pollen.

Blooms April–May.

Helen Hamilton

Blue Curls NATIVE

Trichostema dichotomum   LAMIACEAE Mint Family

Description. The four long, deeply curled blue-stalked stamens projecting from the upper lip are distinctive for this small weedy annual. The enlarged lower lip of the blue to violet flower is a landing platform for pollinating insects searching for nectar. Growing to 2 feet tall, the erect stems are much branched and finely but densely hairy. Hairy, toothless leaves are opposite, thin, and oblong to ovate in shape. Typical of members of the Mint Family, the fruits are 4 small one-seeded nutlets.

Habitat. Blue Curls grows in dry woodlands, disturbed areas, and thin soils around rock outcrops in nearly every county in Virginia. The range is from Maine to Michigan and Missouri and south to Florida and Texas.

Comments. The genus name *Trichostema* is composed of Greek *thrix*, "hair" and *stema*, "stamen," from the hair-like filaments supporting the anthers of the stamen. Referring to the branching stems, *dichotomum* means "forked in pairs."

Blooms August–November.

Helen Hamilton

Bird's-eye Speedwell INTRODUCED

Veronica persica   PLANTAGINACEAE Plantain Family

Description. A cheerful patch of bright-blue flowers in early spring, this small creeping annual is a common lawn weed. Each ¼-inch flower, with 4 lobes streaked with dark blue and a pale center, is on a long stalk from a leaf axil. Stems may reach a foot or so tall, with the main leaves opposite, hairy, ovate to round, and toothed. The small fruits are notched and heart-shaped. Seven other Veronicas, some also lawn weeds, occur on the Coastal Plain. Bird's-eye differs in its larger flowers, growing on stalks (pedicels) in the axils of leaves.

Habitat. Native to Eurasia, Bird's-eye Speedwell is established in gardens, lawns, and fields, even in dry or sandy soil. It ranges over much of North America to Newfoundland and Alaska, and is widespread in Virginia.

Comments. This little plant is named for St. Veronica, whose name is thought to be from Latin *vera*, "true" and Greek *eikon*, "image." Legend pictures St. Veronica, pitying Christ on the way to Calvary, wiping his face with her handkerchief, which received a miraculous "true image" of his features. *Persica* means "of Persia."

Blooms March–June.

Common Bluet

NATIVE

Houstonia caerulea RUBIACEAE Madder Family

Description. Common Bluet spreads by rhizomes and is often found in striking patches of light blue in early spring. The ½-inch pale blue flowers have 4 petals and a yellow center. Small leaves are mostly at the base, with a few pairs of very small stem leaves. This delicate perennial blooms the first year and then potentially annually.

Habitat. Growing in fields, on grassy slopes, in thickets, and in lawns on acid soils from Nova Scotia and Quebec to Wisconsin and south to Georgia and Arkansas, Common Bluet is reported from nearly every county in Virginia.

Comments. These plants are also known as Quaker Ladies because of their similarity to the shape of a Quaker lady's hat. The genus name honors William Houstoun (1695–1733), a Scottish physician and botanist who, as a ship's surgeon, collected plants in Mexico and the West Indies. *Caerulea* is Latin for "blue." Cherokee mothers treated bedwetters with bluet-leaf tea. Tiny flies pollinate bluets, and the Eastern Tailed Blue butterfly also visits the flowers.

Blooms April–July.

Phillip Merritt

Wild Pansy

NATIVE

Viola bicolor   VIOLACEAE Violet Family

Description. Blooming all over fields, meadows, and roadsides, Wild Pansy is a welcome sign of spring. The flower has 5 pale-blue petals, the lower purplish-veined, and a yellow center. The petals are much larger than the sepals. The alternate spoon-shaped leaves are flanked by paired leafy appendages (stipules) that are deeply cut into narrow lobes. The plant often forms colonies so dense as to create a groundcover. This is a winter or spring annual, reproducing by seeds that are ejected mechanically from the pods. Widely established in Virginia, the introduced European Field Pansy *(V. arvensis)* has cream-colored flowers with a deep yellow center and petals about equaling the sepals or less.

Habitat. Wild Pansy tolerates sandy, clayey, and limy soils and is found in most of the eastern U.S. except the extreme north. The only pansy native to North America, it grows wild in every county in Virginia.

Comments. Wild Pansy is most commonly known as Johnny-jump-up, so named for the plant's quick growth in the spring. Caterpillars of fritillary butterflies and moths feed on the foliage of many species of violets. Bees and small butterflies are attracted to the nectar and pollen of the flowers.

Blooms March–May.

Carolina Wild Petunia NATIVE

Ruellia caroliniensis ACANTHACEAE Acanthus Family

Description. Resembling the annual garden petunia, the perennial Wild Petunia produces crowded clusters of 5-lobed flowers, 1 to 2 inches long and wide, from the axils of the middle and upper leaves. The trumpet-shaped flowers vary in color from pale lavender to medium bluish purple and contain 4 stamens. Each blossom lasts only a day or two, but new flowers form in succession. Leaves are opposite, ovate to lanceolate, with fine long hairs or nearly glabrous. The plant grows no more than 2 feet tall, erect but a little straggly. A similar species, Smooth Wild Petunia *(R. strepens)* has stems minutely hairy on 2 opposite sides. Its calyx lobes are lanceolate, over $\frac{1}{16}$ inch broad. In Carolina Wild Petunia the lobes are extremely narrow, under $\frac{1}{16}$ inch.

Habitat. Wild Petunia can be seen along roadsides and in moist or dry woods across most of Virginia. The plant is found from New Jersey to Indiana and south to Florida and Texas.

Comments. This plant was named for the early French herbalist Jean Ruelle (1474–1537); *strepens* means "rustling," from the explosive seed capsules.

Blooms May–September.

Field Garlic

Field Garlic

Field Garlic

Wild Leek

Field Garlic

Allium vineale   AMARYLLIDACAE Amaryllis Family

Description. Field Garlic is a bulb-forming perennial with a globe-like flower head at the top of each slender stem. Flowers are purple to green or white with 6 small tepals. Tiny aerial bulblets (center) are often produced instead of flowers and are smooth and shiny with tail-like leaf sprouts. Erect basal leaves can be 2 feet long, hollow below, and nearly round. The plant is also known as Onion Grass since all parts give off a strong garlic odor when crushed. The stately Wild Leek (*A. ampeloprasum*, right) is another introduced species, locally known as Yorktown Onion. The purple 3-inch flower heads on 4-foot stems with flat leaves form a stunning display along the York River on the Colonial Parkway. The plant is protected by the National Park Service.

Habitat. A native of Europe, Field Garlic is a noxious pest of lawns, pastures, and meadows. The plant occurs in nearly every county in Virginia and throughout the eastern and central U.S. Wild Leek is found in the southern U.S., California, and in only a few counties in Virginia.

Comments. *Allium* is the ancient Latin name for garlic. Although the taste is rather strong, there has been some use of this species in salads and as a cooked vegetable.

Blooms May–June.

181

Wild Ginger

NATIVE

Asarum canadense   ARISTOLOCHIACEAE Birthwort Family

Description. Covering the flower, soft, hairy leaves are heart-shaped and grow in pairs 6 to 12 inches tall. Three-lobed purplish flowers, hairy on the outside, form close to the ground and are bell-shaped with pointed, sometimes reflexed tips. When seeds ripen, small oily appendages attract ants, which carry the seeds underground. Dispersal is facilitated and the seeds are protected from animals.

Habitat. Found in rich woods, Wild Ginger usually forms colonies from spreading rhizomes. This plant prefers nutrient-rich soils such as those found in calcareous ravines in the Coastal Plain. Widespread across Virginia, the plant ranges from Quebec and Minnesota and south to North Carolina and Louisiana.

Comments. Wild Ginger is not related to Culinary Ginger *(Zingiber officinale)*, but the rhizomes have a ginger-like fragrance, and early settlers cooked the root in sugared water. However, the plants may contain poisonous compounds not suitable for consumption. Two antibiotic compounds present corroborate its use by Native Americans and European settlers as a poultice to treat wounds. Although Wild Ginger flowers are self-pollinated, flies that enter the flowers may be attracted to the color or odor of the flower, similar to that of decomposing flesh.

Blooms April–May.

Blue Mistflower

Conoclinium coelestinum   ASTERACEAE Aster Family

Description. Blue Mistflower has flat-topped clusters of soft, fluffy violet-blue flowers on 1- to 3-foot branching stalks. Each flower head consists of many tiny 5-petaled disk flowers whose long styles cause the fuzzy appearance of this flower; there are no ray flowers on this member of the Aster Family. The densely hairy stems bear toothed, somewhat triangular-shaped leaves in pairs on short petioles.

Habitat. Preferring moist soils in full sun or partial shade, this plant is easily grown in average, medium, well-drained soils. Blue Mistflower grows wild at woods edges, on streambanks, and in ditches, meadows, and fields in nearly every county in Virginia. The range is from New York to Illinois and Kansas and south to Florida and Texas. This perennial plant spreads by rhizomes (thick underground stems producing roots and shoots of new plants) and can be aggressive in ideal growing conditions.

Comments. Attractive to bees and butterflies, Blue Mistflower is also known as Wild Ageratum because the flowers resemble those of the shorter (6- to 12-inch) annual, Dwarf Ageratum *(Ageratum houstonianum),* sold in garden centers as bedding plants.

Blooms July–October.

Left: Helen Hamilton   Right: Phillip Merritt

Robin's Plantain

NATIVE

Erigeron pulchellus   ASTERACEAE Aster Family

Description. While the flowers of Robin's Plantain somewhat resemble asters, the rays are more slender and numerous, 50 or more. Distinctive lavender-blue to white flowers with yellow centers appear singly or in several-headed clusters. The single soft, hollow, flowering stalk to 2 feet tall comes from a rosette of oval basal leaves, each up to 5 inches long and 3 inches across. Both the stems and the leaves are softly hairy. The plant spreads by elongate creeping stems (stolons).

Habitat. Robin's Plantain is found in moist woods and on streambanks, growing on limy soils. In Virginia it is frequent in the Mountain and Piedmont regions; on the Coastal Plain, the calcareous fossil-bearing soils exposed in ravines provide suitable habitat. The range extends from Maine to Ontario and east-central Minnesota and south to Georgia, Mississippi, and east Texas.

Comments. The genus name comes from Greek *eri*, "early," and *geron*, "old man," meaning "old man in the spring," and refers to the fluffy white seed heads and the early flowering and fruiting of many species; *pulchellus* means "handsome."

Blooms April–June.

Seig Kopinitz

Blazing Star NATIVE

Liatris pilosa (L. graminifolia)   ASTERACEAE Aster Family

Description. Blazing Star is well named for a dense spike-like arrangement of pink-purple flower heads that, differing from most plants, bloom from the top of the stem downward. Heads are of disk flowers only (no ray flowers). This is a wand-like, perennial herb with stems growing 1 to 3 feet tall. Soft, very narrow leaves are alternate on the stem, relatively numerous, and 8 inches or more long.

Habitat. Blazing Star occurs in dry, open woods, especially in sandy soil among pines. This plant grows well in full sun and well-drained soil; it is drought tolerant but cannot adapt to wet ground. Widespread across Virginia, it grows from New Jersey and southern Pennsylvania to Georgia, northwest Florida, and Alabama.

Comments. Several members of the genus appear to have medicinal properties. The tuberous roots have a turpentine odor and contain an oil with a bitter taste; a decoction of the root is used for sore throat and as a diuretic to remove metabolic wastes. Leaves of some species contain coumarin, a blood-thinning chemical, and, like so many other plants, were once used to treat snakebite.

Blooms August–November.

Big-headed Aster

NATIVE

Symphyotrichum grandiflorum   ASTERACEAE   Aster Family
(Aster grandiflorus)

Description. Big-headed Aster is well named; its yellow disk (reddish in age) is surrounded by reddish-purple rays ranging from ¾ inch to nearly 1½ inches long. Each of the many flower heads is solitary at the tip of an elongate branchlet studded with small, oblong to linear-lanceolate bracts. The lowest leaves soon shrivel; the upper are stiff, harshly short-hairy, usually small and bractlike (up to 1½ inches long), and numerous. The plant often has multiple ascending branches and a shrub-like appearance.

Habitat. Big-headed Aster provides a vibrant splash of color in dry, sandy, open pine or oak woods, in old fields, and along roadsides scattered across its very restricted range—the Piedmont and Coastal Plain of Virginia and the Carolinas. Other showy, fall-flowering blue-rayed asters include Clasping Heart-leaf Aster *(S. undulatum)* and Clasping Aster *(S. patens)* in these same habitats, and New York Aster *(S. novibelgii)* in fresh and brackish marshes, swamps, and other wet habitats.

Comments. Nectar produced by this aster is appreciated by many butterflies, including the Fiery Skipper.

Blooms September–November.

Teta Kain

New York Ironweed NATIVE

Vernonia noveboracensis   ASTERACEAE   Aster Family

Description. Handsome plants of imposing stature and marvelous color, New York Ironweed has rich reddish-purple flower heads that lack rays and are composed of disk flowers only. The small flower heads occur in loosely branched, usually flat-topped, terminal clusters. The erect stems grow 3 to 10 feet tall. Leaves are alternate, lance-shaped, and more or less toothed. One-seeded fruits (achenes) are topped with numerous purple or dark brown bristles and scales. Upland Ironweed *(V. glauca),* a species of drier habitats, has leaves less than 4 times as long as wide, and the achene is crowned with whitish or yellowish bristles.

Habitat. Usually found in low wet areas of woods, fields, and streambanks, New York Ironweed is widespread across Virginia and ranges from Massachusetts to Florida inland to western Pennsylvania, eastern Kentucky, and Alabama.

Comments. The common name may refer to the difficulty of pulling up the plant without a will of iron, or the "iron" could describe the tall, sturdy stems. The genus was named for William Vernon, an English botanist who collected in Maryland in the late 1600s; *noveboracensis* means "of New York." The flowers are butterfly magnets, especially for the Eastern Tiger Swallowtail.

Blooms July–September.

Helen Hamilton

Downy Lobelia

Lobelia puberula   CAMPANULACEAE Bellflower Family

Description. A pretty little perennial growing to 1 to 3 feet, Downy Lobelia has both the flowers and their bracts crowded into a terminal, elongate, usually one-sided group. The violet-blue flowers are ¾ inch long with 5 petals fused into a tube, the 3 lower petal lobes projecting downward, the upper two curling upward. The flowers of Indian Tobacco *(L. inflata),* a somewhat weedy annual species, are ⅜ inch and blue to white, and the bell-like calyx inflates over the fruit.

Habitat. Downy Lobelia is found from New Jersey to Florida and west to Illinois and Texas, and in most of the eastern and Piedmont counties of Virginia. The plant prefers wet soil in open woods and clearings in sun or shade. Blooming later than its relatives Cardinal Flower (page 133) and Great Blue Lobelia (page 171), this species is a nice addition to a late summer garden.

Comments. The genus is dedicated to Matthias de l'Obel (1538–1616), Flemish herbalist and physician to James I of England. The species name comes from the Latin *puber* meaning "downy" and refers to the short hairs on the stem and leaves. Like other Lobelias, this species contains very poisonous alkaloids.

Blooms July–October.

Helen Hamilton

Clasping Venus' Looking-glass   NATIVE

Triodanis perfoliata   CAMPANULACEAE Bellflower Family

Description. Vivid purple-blue flowers, ½ inch wide, perch in leaf axils along the upper ends of slender, wandlike stems. Small round-ovate leaves, usually toothed, are without petioles and clasp the stem. Flowers lower on the stem remain closed and budlike but produce seeds by self-fertilization. This annual, simple or sparingly branched, becomes 1 to 3 feet tall. Some southern plants are distinguished as *T. biflora*. Such plants have but a single expanded flower—the terminal one—the leaves not clasping and longer than wide, but hybridization with *T. perfoliata* is so frequent the validity of this species is doubtful.

Habitat. Clasping Venus' Looking-glass grows in various habitats in poor soil such as abandoned fields and along railroads and roadsides, especially where gravelly or sandy. The plant is found in every county of Virginia and from Maine to British Columbia and south to tropical America.

Comments. *Triodanis* means "three teeth," referring to the seed, and *perfoliata* comes from the Latin for "through the leaf," referring to the cup-shaped leaves, which almost surround the stem. A charming folk tale about a European species tells of a drop of water that can collect in the leaf axil, acting as a mirror for Venus.

Blooms April–June.

189

Groundnut

NATIVE

Apios americana   FABACEAE Pea Family

Description. A perennial vine with stems 2 to 10 feet long, Groundnut twines upon and through the shrubbery beneath the forest canopy. Fragrant purple-brown flowers are clustered on short stalks from leaf axils. The feather-compound leaves are arranged alternately along the stem, with 5 to 7 oval, sharp-pointed leaflets. The fruit is a slender pod 2 to 5 inches long and edible, as are the cooked seeds. This legume has a cord-like rootstalk with edible tubers, which the Indians and the early settlers gathered for food. The tubers can be used in soups and stews or fried like potatoes. Crunchy and nutritious with 3 times as much protein as potatoes, Groundnut is being developed for domestication. As in other legumes, nodules on the roots of the plant fix atmospheric nitrogen, so the plant would not require much fertilizer.

Habitat. Groundnut grows in shady, moist areas and ranges from Quebec to Minnesota and South Dakota and south to Florida and Texas. This plant is found in every county in Virginia, growing in moist woods and along streambanks.

Comments. The caterpillars of the Silver-spotted Skipper feed on the foliage of this plant. *Apios* means "pear" in Greek and alludes to the shape of the tubers.

Blooms June–August.

Butterfly Pea NATIVE

Clitoria mariana   FABACAE   Pea Family

Description. Butterfly Pea has beautiful 2-inch-long flowers, mostly solitary and pale blue-lilac with darker veins. The stems are twining, bearing compound leaves with 3 broadly lance-shaped leaflets. This species is easily confused with Spurred Butterfly Pea *(Centrosema virginianum)*, which has a calyx-tube around the base of the flower with slender lobes, not short teeth.

Habitat. This plant prefers acidic soils in wooded areas and clearings and is drought tolerant. Growing in almost every county in Virginia, Butterfly Pea ranges from New Jersey west to Missouri and Oklahoma and south to Florida, Texas, and Arizona. In Virginia, *Centrosema* is confined to the Coastal Plain and southern Piedmont.

Comments. The shape of the two small keel petals has inspired the name of this genus. Different species of *Clitoria* have been used to enhance fertility, to control menstrual discharge, to treat gonorrhea, and as a sexual stimulant. Some users of folk medicine follow the Doctrine of Signatures, a myth that plant structures resembling portions of the human body indicate their ability to provide remedies for those parts.

Blooms June–August.

Trailing Lespedeza

NATIVE

Lespedeza procumbens

FABACEAE Pea Family

Description. Trailing Lespedeza is well named for its sprawling growth habit. This perennial has stems to 4 feet long and both stems and leaves are covered with soft spreading hairs. The 3 leaflets are oval, rounded at the base and tip. Clusters of 8 to 12 violet flowers are at the ends of stalks much longer than the leaves. The one-seeded pod (legume) is ¼-inch long, oval to round, pointed, and covered with spreading hairs. Creeping Lespedeza *(L. repens)* has smooth stems, leaves, and fruits, or with appressed hairs, and 3 to 8 flowers. Slender Lespedeza *(L. virginica)* has stout, stiff erect stems.

Habitat. Trailing Lespedeza is found in dry, open, sandy, or rocky woods and clearings, ranging from New Hampshire to Wisconsin and south to Georgia, western Florida, and Texas. These 3 native species are common over most of Virginia. Other native and introduced species of *Lespedeza* also inhabit the Coastal Plain.

Comments. The genus honors Vincente de Cespedez (misspelled de Lespedez), Spanish governor of East Florida in the late 1700s. These plants are commonly known as Bush Clovers.

Blooms July–September.

192

Dwarf Iris

Southern Blue Flag

Yellow Flag

Southern Blue Flag

NATIVE

Iris virginica

IRIDACEAE Iris Family

Description. A tall, bold wildflower growing up to 3 feet tall, Southern Blue Flag has pale-green sword-like leaves in strong, flat, vertical fans. The showy flowers are more than 3 inches wide, and deep blue-violet with yellow and white markings. The 3 outer tepals are called "falls," the 3 inner, erect ones "standards." The 3 style branches are also petaloid.

Habitat. This native perennial grows best in wet, boggy, acidic, sandy soils. The foliage is strongest in partial shade, but the flowers bloom best in full sun. The plant spreads by rhizomes and will form colonies in optimum growing conditions. Native to the eastern and central U.S. and Canada, in Virginia Southern Blue Flag is found mostly in the eastern counties. Dwarf Iris (*Iris verna*, top right) is shorter and fragrant, blooms at the same time, and is found only in the southern coastal counties. Introduced in the mid-1800s as an ornamental from Eurasia or Northern Africa, Yellow Flag (*Iris pseudacorus*, bottom right) is now established in eastern and western counties of Virginia. This invasive plant can withstand a wide variety of conditions, outcompeting native species.

Comments. *Iris* is Greek for "rainbow," possibly referring to the variety of colors seen in iris. "Flag" is from the middle English *flagge,* meaning "rush" or "reed," in reference to the habitat of these plants.

Blooms April–May.

Helen Hamilton

Blue-eyed Grass

NATIVE

Sisyrinchium angustifolium

IRIDACEAE Iris Family

Description. Blue-eyed Grass is not a grass and does not have a blue center! A member of the Iris Family, this clump-forming perennial grows from a tuft of narrow grass-like leaves no more than 12 inches high. Delicate flowers emerge from a spathe, a pair of bracts borne at the top of the narrow, winged flowering stems. Less than an inch wide, the flowers consist of 6 violet-blue sepals and petals, each tipped with a bristle. Golden-yellow stamens and pistils in the center form a yellow "eye." Small round fruit capsules appear in summer. Eastern Blue-eyed Grass *(S. atlanticum)* is very similar, but the flowering stems are narrower, less than ⅛ inch wide.

Habitat. Widespread across Virginia, Blue-eyed Grass is found in meadows, ditches, grassy places, and damp woods, ranging from Newfoundland to Minnesota and south to Florida and Texas. Eastern Blue-eyed Grass grows in some counties of the Coastal Plain and western Virginia.

Comments. The genus name is Greek, *sys* for "pig" and *rynchus* for "snout," referring to "swine snout," as the roots were much sought after by pigs. Native Americans used root tea for diarrhea in children and treated worms and stomachaches with plant tea.

Blooms April–June.

Louise Menges

Ground Ivy

Glechoma hederacea   LAMIACEAE Mint Family

Description. Ground Ivy is an evergreen perennial with creeping stems that root at the nodes. Like other members of the Mint Family, it has square stems and its foliage has a mint-like odor when mowed. Scalloped roundish or kidney-shaped leaves are often purplish, growing opposite on the stem on long stalks. Small, ½-inch-long blue-violet flowers typically occur in clusters of 3 in the angle between the stem and leaf stalk. After the flowers, tiny egg-shaped brown nutlets appear.

Habitat. A native of Eurasia, Ground Ivy is common in roadsides, lawns, moist woods, and disturbed habitats. Primarily a weed of turfgrass and landscapes, this introduced plant is widespread across Virginia and throughout the northern and southeastern U.S.

Comments. The genus name comes from an old Greek name for pennyroyal or other mints. *Hederacea* means "resembling *Hedera*," English Ivy. High in vitamin C, leaf tea was used traditionally to treat headaches, sore throat, and as a spring tonic. The fresh plant is nutritious in salads and as a steamed vegetable. Before Common Hops *(Humulus lupulus)* was introduced to England, the leaves were used by the early Saxons to clarify their beers.

Blooms March–June.

Phillip Merritt

Self-heal

Prunella vulgaris var. *lanceolata*   LAMIACEAE Mint Family

Description. This familiar lawn weed is recognized by the cylindric terminal spikes of purple flowers. Individual flowers are about ½ inch long with 2 lips, the upper lip arched and the lower drooping and 3-lobed. Leaves are opposite, 1 to 3 inches long, lanceolate or variable in shape with somewhat wedged-shaped bases. Self-heal is a sprawling plant, often growing no more than 6 to 12 inches in height. The stems are somewhat 4-angled, a usual characteristic of the Mint Family. The introduced Eurasian Self-heal, *P. vulgaris* var. *vulgaris*, has more flowers on the spikes, and the bases of the leaves are rounded. Because of extensive hybridization, however, it is often difficult to discriminate between these varieties.

Habitat. Self-heal is a common perennial weed in gardens, fields, and roadsides and occurs in every county in Virginia. The range extends across the U.S. and Canada, the species nearly cosmopolitan.

Comments. The genus may derive from the German *breaume*, "quinsy," a throat infection. Also known as Heal-all, leaf tea of this plant has been used for sore throats, mouth sores, and other medicinal purposes. The plant contains compounds that are antibiotic and hypotensive, as well as antioxidant components.

Blooms April–December.

Seig Kopinitz

Helmet Skullcap

NATIVE

Scutellaria integrifolia

LAMIACEAE Mint Family

Description. The purple flowers of this perennial are about 1 inch long with an arched upper lip and flaring lower lip. The fused petals form a hood ("helmet") over the lower lip, which has 2 distinct white spots. Leaves are opposite on square, finely hairy stems up to 2 feet tall. The narrow, mostly toothless leaves are distinctive for this species; the lower leaves are broader and slightly toothed.

Habitat. Helmet Skullcap grows best in full sun and wet soil in fields and borders of woods and clearings throughout Virginia. The range is from Massachusetts to Florida and Texas, especially on the Coastal Plain, and inland to Ohio and Tennessee. Two other species with smaller flowers are widespread in Virginia, Hairy Skullcap *(S. elliptica)* and Mad Dog Skullcap *(S. lateriflora)*. In both, the upper leaves are toothed; in Mad Dog Skullcap, the flowering racemes are mostly lateral from the axils of foliage leaves.

Comments. The many different Skullcaps are recognized by the tiny transverse hump on the top of the calyx (group of sepals) at the base of the flower. In Latin *scutella* means "little dish," referring to this lobe. *Integrifolia* means "entire-leaved," i.e., toothless. Mad Dog Skullcap had a reputation, since discounted, as a cure for rabies.

Blooms May–July.

American Germander   NATIVE

Teucrium canadense   LAMIACEAE Mint Family

Description. Growing to 3 feet tall on stiff square stems, this perennial produces lavender-pink flowers in terminal spike-like clusters. While the flowers of members of the Mint Family generally have 2 lips, in this species the flowers appear to have a single, 5-lobed lip. The upper part is very short with 4 protruding stamens, and the lowest lobe is long and flattened. The leaves are aromatic, opposite, and oblong, pointed at the tip and rounded at the base with teeth along the edges. The stem and undersides of the leaves are often silvery-pubescent. As in other mints, the fruit is 4 nutlets.

Habitat. American Germander is found in all counties of Virginia, common in rich woods, moist thickets, and on shores and salt marshes. The range extends throughout most of the U.S. and southern Canada.

Comments. The genus name is possibly derived from Teucer, a Trojan king who used a related plant medicinally. Leaf tea from this plant has been used traditionally to induce menstruation, urination, and sweating, and leaves were applied as an antiseptic dressing.

Blooms June–July.

Saltmarsh Loosestrife · Saltmarsh Loosestrife · Purple Loosestrife

Helen Hamilton

Saltmarsh Loosestrife NATIVE

Lythrum lineare   LYTHRACEAE Loosestrife Family

Description. A salt-tolerant plant of marshes, this smooth, slender, erect, much-branched perennial grows to 3 feet tall. Narrow leaves are mostly opposite, 2 inches long at the bottom of the plant and smaller toward the top. Pale lilac to white flowers grow in the leaf axils.

Habitat. Saltmarsh Loosestrife grows in brackish marshes, at pond edges, and in meadows on the Coastal Plain from New Jersey to Florida and Louisiana. In Virginia, it occurs only in those counties bordering brackish waters. Purple Loosestrife (*L. salicaria*, right, see also page 158) is a highly invasive species with showy reddish-purple flowers, stamens mostly 12, in dense, leafy, spike-like clusters more than a foot long. Imported from Eurasia, it has been found in several areas in Virginia and is widespread across the U.S. and Canada. It is listed as invasive in many states, where laws prohibit its sale and propagation. Of little value to wildlife, it crowds out native wetland vegetation, even cattails (!) and forms extensive stands, sometimes of thousands of acres.

Comments. In the Roman army *Lythrum salicaria* was called Lytron, Greek for "blood," possibly for its red flower. *Salicaria* refers to the leaves, narrow like those of willow (*Salix* spp.)

Blooms July–October.

Putty-root Orchid

NATIVE

Aplectrum hyemale   ORCHIDACEAE Orchid Family

Description. Putty-root Orchid is easily found in the leaf litter in winter as a single large oval leaf. Each corrugated leaf is uniquely pin-striped, with parallel silvery-white veins alternating with green. Adapted to shady deciduous forests, the leaf is present only when the trees are leafless. In late May or early June, the flower stalk arises, carrying several small purplish-green blossoms with 3 sepals and 3 petals, the lip petal mostly white.

Habitat. Found in calcareous ravines in the Coastal Plain, this orchid grows in rich deciduous woods and moist soil in most counties of Virginia and in the eastern half of the U.S. and southern Canada. Putty-root Orchid will spread underground through the growth of its tubers, forming large colonies.

Comments. The only other species of this genus is native to Japan. *Aplectrum* comes from Latin, meaning that the flowers are "without spurs." *Hyemale* means "winter" and refers to the solitary leaf that persists all winter. The common name refers to a mucilaginous substance produced from crushed roots. It was used to mend crockery by early settlers and for medicinal purposes by Native Americans.

Blooms May–June.

Lily-leaved Twayblade

NATIVE

Liparis liliifolia ORCHIDACEAE Orchid Family

Description. This small orchid lacks bright colors and, blending into the background, can be overlooked. The 4- to 10-inch flowering stem bears 5 to 30 flowers on slender reddish stalks. The ½-inch-long greenish and purplish flowers have broad, nearly flat translucent lips prominently veined with reddish purple. Fertilized flowers produce elliptical seed capsules, which split open to release numerous tiny seeds distributed by the wind. The plant bears only two leaves ("twayblade") in a pair at the base, 3 to 6 inches long and half as much across. They are shiny medium green, oval, and with smooth margins, slightly bent.

Habitat. Lily-leaved Twayblade grows in rich moist woods and floodplains in every county in Virginia. This orchid adapts to many soil types and prefers partial sunlight or light shade, but it cannot survive without the presence of a specific fungus in the soil. The range is from Maine to Minnesota and south to Georgia and Arkansas, and also in China.

Comments. The genus name *Liparis* comes from Greek *liparos,* meaning "fat," or "shining," referring to the smooth and lustrous leaves. This orchid is endangered in several states.

Blooms May–July.

Purple False Foxglove   NATIVE

Agalinis purpurea   OROBANCHACEAE Broomrape Family

Description. Attractive rose-purple flowers grace wet areas in early fall. An inch or more long, the bell-shaped flowers have yellow lines and purple spots within, opening out into 5 rounded lobes. The flowers are followed by subglobose capsules that split, releasing numerous tiny seeds into the wind. The leaves are very narrow and mostly opposite, with smooth edges. These annual plants are otherwise rather inconspicuous, slender with wiry branches, and grow to 3 feet tall.

Habitat. Purple False Foxglove can grow in full sun or part shade but requires moist, sandy, or peaty soil. The plant is found in the eastern and central U.S. and Canada and south to Mexico in bogs and shores. Saltmarsh False Foxglove *(A. maritima)* is a similar species with flowers half as large. Occurring only in the coastal counties of Virginia, its preferred habitat is salt marshes.

Comments. Formerly placed in the Figwort Family and in the genus *Gerardia*, species of *Agalinis* are hemiparasitic on the roots of grasses. The tubular flowers attract bumblebees and other long-tongued bees, which visit the flowers for nectar and pollen. Purple False Foxglove is the host plant to the Buckeye butterfly, as the caterpillars feed on the foliage.

Blooms August–October.

Purple
Passionflower

Yellow
Passionflower

Left: Helen Hamilton   Right: Louise Menges

Purple Passionflower NATIVE

Passiflora incarnata   PASSIFLORACEAE Passionflower Family

Description. This tropical-looking flower grows on an herbaceous vine up to 25 feet long, climbing with tendrils or sprawling along the ground. Arising on short stalks, intricate, 3-inch lavender flowers have a fringe (corona) of wavy, hair-like segments, banded with purple and overtopping the 5 sepals and 5 petals. Three elongate styles extending from the ovary dominate the center of the flower. Leaves are 3-lobed with toothed margins. Another name, Maypop, comes from the hollow yellow fruits that pop when crushed. The blossoms of Yellow Passionflower (*P. lutea*, right) are smaller, pale yellow, the leaves only shallowly lobed and toothless.

Habitat. These plants prefer rich soil, moist or dry, and full sun, growing in pine woods, thickets, and fencerows in the southeastern and central U.S. Both occur widely across Virginia.

Comments. "Passionflower" refers to the floral parts said to represent aspects of the Crucifixion story (the Passion). Chemicals in the plant combat insomnia and anxiety. Native Americans used it as an aphrodisiac and cultivated the plant for the edible fruits. The leaves furnish food for the caterpillars of the Variegated Fritillary butterfly.

Blooms May–August.

Phillip Merritt

Lopseed

Phryma leptostachya   PHRYMACEAE Lopseed Family

Description. This perennial is easy to identify in the field but is often overlooked, with its slender, leafless spike of tiny (¼-inch-long) 2-lipped purple to white flowers. They are arranged in pairs and, when fading and forming seeds, hang down oddly ("lopped down") against the stem. Lopseed grows 1 to 3 feet tall on branching stems that are purple and 4-angled. The ovate 2-inch leaves are opposite, softly hairy, and coarsely toothed, the lower ones long-stalked.

Habitat. Growing in moist woods in every county in Virginia, Lopseed ranges from Quebec to Manitoba and south to Florida and Texas. On the Coastal Plain it is chiefly found in areas underlain with marl. A nearly identical plant occurs from India to Japan. This distribution, in which members of distinct groups survived extinction from geological events only in east Asia and eastern North America, is of major significance to plant geographers.

Comments. This species had been placed in the Verbena Family but is now back to its earlier status as a separate family. The species name *leptostachya* comes from Latin *leptos* for "thin" and *stachya* for "spike," referring to the slender spikes of flowers. Origin of the genus name is unknown.

Blooms June–August.

204

Blue Toadflax

Nuttallanthus canadensis
(Linaria canadensis)

PLANTAGINACEAE Plantain Family

Description. While the flowers are small and the stems slender, Blue Toadflax grows in conspicuous profusion in early spring; its light blue-violet flowers in an elongate cluster are easy to identify. The flowers are about ½ inch long; the upper lip is 2-lobed, the lower 3-lobed with 2 small white ridges. A long, thread-like spur at the base projects backward and downward. From a basal rosette of prostrate leafy stems, erect flowering stems grow to 2 feet tall. Stem leaves are long, thin, and wispy, usually alternate. Many sandy roadsides have a haze of blue from Blue Toadflax colonies in bloom.

Habitat. This annual or biennial grows in full sun or partial shade in open, dry sites and abandoned fields, usually sandy. The plant is found in eastern and central counties of Virginia and ranges from Quebec to Minnesota and south to Florida and Mexico and on the Pacific Coast.

Comments. The leaves resemble those of flax; the older genus name is from Latin *linum*, for "flax." The current genus honors Thomas Nuttall (1789–1859), a British-born naturalist active in western North America.

Blooms March–May.

Phillip Merritt

Smooth Beardtongue   NATIVE

Penstemon laevigatus   PLANTAGINACEAE Plantain Family

Description. More than 3 feet tall, this perennial has trumpet-shaped pale purple flowers in terminal clusters. The corolla is narrowly tubular at the base, abruptly enlarging into the throat. The petals flare outward, revealing 4 fertile stamens with smooth brown anthers and a sterile stamen with a yellowish beard. The fruit is a capsule with numerous seeds. Lance-shaped dark-green leaves are up to 5 inches long, hairless beneath and opposite on the stems. Southern Beardtongue *(P. australis)* has pink to violet flowers, the tube gradually enlarged to the throat, and is finely hairy throughout.

Habitat. Smooth Beardtongue grows in meadows and moist or dry woods in full sun or partial shade. The range is from Maine to Michigan and Illinois and south to Georgia, Mississippi, and Arkansas. Southern Beardtongue prefers sandy soil, ranging from southeast Virginia to Florida and Alabama. Cultivars and hybrids of *Penstemon* are prized by gardeners.

Comments. The common name "beardtongue" refers to the tuft of hairs on one of the stamens. *Penstemon* is derived from *pente,* "five," and *stemon,* "stamen," in reference to the fifth infertile stamen. Hummingbirds and bumblebees are attracted to the nectar in the narrow base of the flowers.

Blooms May–June.

206

Sea Lavender

NATIVE

Limonium carolinianum   PLUMBAGINACEAE Leadwort Family

Description. This plant is easy to recognize, forming a "sea" of small lavender flowers waving across salt marshes in late summer and early fall. A taprooted perennial, it has large, fleshy, lance-shaped leaves that grow mostly from the base of the plant. The stem branches many times, and the flowers mature from the bottom upward. While the 5 petals are purple to lavender, the outside base of the flower (sepals) is white, an unusual combination.

Habitat. Growing in salty soil, Sea Lavender is common in saline or brackish marshes in the coastal counties of Virginia. The range extends along the coast from Labrador south to Florida and west to Texas and northeast Mexico.

Comments. "Leimonion," the ancient Greek name, is presumably derived from *leimon*, a marsh. Our ancestors' druggists sold large quantities for use as an astringent. The 18th-century botanist Mannasseh Cutler, calling it Marsh Rosemary, wrote of a decoction of the roots used as a gargle for cankers and sore throats. The flowers are prized for bouquets and dried arrangements, retaining their color for several years.

Blooms August–October.

Pickerelweed

Pontederia cordata   PONTEDERIACEAE Pickerelweed Family

Description. This perennial is an aquatic plant, with its leaves and flowers above water and portions of the stem underwater. Flower stalks extend 1 to 2 feet above water, the violet-blue flowers densely arranged on an erect spike. Each flower is funnel-shaped with 2 lips, the upper petal marked with yellow. A single leaf-like bract occurs not far below the flowers, while the other leaves arise at the base of the stem. They are erect, soft, oblong, and usually heart-shaped at the base. When mature, the 1-seeded fruits have 6 toothed ridges at the top.

Habitat. Pickerelweed is typically found in shallow, quiet water in marshes and freshwater ditches. In Virginia the plant occurs in the Coastal Plain; it ranges from Nova Scotia to Ontario and Minnesota and south to South America.

Comments. The genus name honors Giulio Pontedera (1688–1756), professor at Padua, Italy. Native Americans used this plant to prevent pregnancy. The ripe seeds are highly nutritious and can be eaten or ground into flour. Bumblebees are said to be the most common pollinators.

Blooms May–October.

208

Dwarf Bluet

Woodland Bluet

Left: Helen Hamilton   Right: Phillip Merritt

Dwarf Bluet

NATIVE

Houstonia pusilla   RUBIACEAE Madder Family

Description. This tiny annual bluet, with purple-violet flowers no more than ¼ inch across, can color a field in early spring. Each blossom consists of a narrow tube ending in 4 petals right-angled around a central reddish eye. The flowers are borne on terminal stalks up to an inch long, from the axils of the ½-inch-long, opposite leaves.

Habitat. Growing in dry soil, fields, and roadsides, Dwarf Bluet is often found on disturbed land from Virginia south to Florida, west to Texas, and north in the interior to Illinois and South Dakota. In Virginia, this plant is found mostly in the Coastal Plain and south-central counties.

Comments. Two similar perennial species grow naturally in the Coastal Plain in Virginia; the pale blue flowers of Common Bluet (*H. caerulea*, page 178) have a yellow eye, while the similar flowers of Woodland Bluet (*H. purpurea*, right) are centered with a pale eye. The paired leaves of Woodland Bluet are broad ovate- to lance-shaped on stems up to 18 inches tall. These two species bloom later than Dwarf Bluet and are found in woodlands and other moist situations.

Blooms March–April.

Field Madder INTRODUCED

Galium sherardia (Sherardia arvensis)   RUBIACEAE Madder Family

Description. Tiny 4-lobed flowers, less than ¼ inch across, pink to lavender, are clustered in leafy terminal heads. The main leaves are rough-hairy, sharp-pointed, and mostly in whorls of 6. The stems are square, sprawling close to the ground, to several feet long. While low in stature, this annual plant with its tiny flowers can be so dominant as to attract attention. The fruit is a pair of one-seeded segments.

Habitat. A native of western Eurasia and northern Africa, Field Madder grows as a weed in waste places and on cultivated ground; it is considered a lawn weed on the East Coast. In Virginia this introduced species is scattered through the coastal and mountain counties as well as in the extreme southwest. The plant now occurs in eastern and western areas of the U.S. and Canada.

Comments. The genus comes from Greek *gala*, "milk," from the use of some species in curdling milk. The species was named for English botanist Dr. William Sherard (1659–1728). Field Madder can be confused with species of bedstraw, but the leaves of Field Madder are sharp-pointed and smaller than those of bedstraws, and the general habit and habitat are different.

Blooms February–August.

210

Jan Newton

Bird's-foot Violet
NATIVE

Viola pedata   VIOLACEAE Violet Family

Description. This is a beautiful violet of early spring, easy to identify with its large violet-blue flowers and bird's-foot-shaped leaves. Each leaf is deeply divided palmately into 3 to 5 lobes, while a lobe may be further subdivided into 2 to 3 smaller lobes. Toward the throat of the flower, the lower petal is white with fine violet lines that function as nectar guides for pollinators. In a bicolored form of Bird's-foot Violet the 2 upper petals are deep violet, while the lower 3 are pale purple or lilac. Distinctive for this species are the 5 orange stamens protruding conspicuously in the center of the flower.

Habitat. Bird's-foot Violet prefers full sun and dry conditions but will tolerate a little shade and some moisture if the site is well drained. It grows in dry fields, on shady roadsides, and in open woods in most counties of Virginia, ranging from Maine to Minnesota south to Florida and Texas.

Comments. Compared with those of other violets, the flowers of this species attract more butterflies and skippers. Since the petals are often held close to the ground, they provide easy access for insects. The caterpillars of fritillary butterflies feed on the foliage and flowers; the surface of the seeds has a sugary gel that attracts ants which then carry off the seeds, aiding in dispersal.

Blooms March–May.

Common Blue Violet

Confederate Violet

Common Blue Violet NATIVE

Viola sororia   VIOLACEAE Violet Family

Description. The deep purple-blue color of this little flower is a welcome sign of spring. Heart-shaped leaves with wavy edges form a basal rosette growing no more than 8 inches tall. The leaves and the flowers are borne on separate stems, the flowers a little taller than the leaves.

Habitat. The most familiar of several blue violets on the Coastal Plain, Common Blue Violet prefers partial sun or light shade and moist to average conditions. The preferred soil is a rich loam with above-average amounts of organic matter. Found in most of the counties in Virginia and widely distributed across the eastern and central U.S., the plant often grows in lawns that are not mowed too closely. Common Blue Violets spread easily by rhizomes and seeds, and many gardeners use them as groundcover. The plant distributes seeds by mechanical ejection from the three-parted seed capsules. Zillions of tiny, heart-shaped leaves appear only weeks later, radiating out from the mother plant.

Comments. The flowers and young leaves are edible and can be added to salads in small amounts. The caterpillars of fritillary butterflies feed on the leaves. A variety with whitish petals and violet markings (at right above) is known as Confederate Violet.

Blooms March–June.

Jack-in-the-pulpit

NATIVE

Arisaema triphyllum ARACEAE Arum Family

Description. The unusual inflorescence is a leafy sheath (spathe) of green or purplish brown, often striped, which curves gracefully over the club-shaped spadix—the "Jack," or preacher, in his canopied pulpit. Minute flowers are borne on the base of the spadix. One or two leaves on long stalks rise above the flower. Leaves are 3-parted, with two of the leaflets at right angles to the central one. The fruit is a cluster of glossy green berries, becoming scarlet. Three varieties, based on minor differences in spathe shape and color, are recognized in Virginia.

Habitat. This perennial requires humus-rich moist soils in sun or shade and needs little care when left undisturbed in a woodland garden. Growing in rich woods and bogs from Nova Scotia to North Dakota and south to Florida and Texas, it is found in nearly every county in Virginia.

Comments. Jack-in-the-pulpit is also known as Indian Turnip because Native Americans gathered the fleshy taproot as a vegetable and used the dried root for many conditions. However, all parts of the plant contain calcium oxalate crystals when fresh and are intensely irritating. Pollination by fungus gnats and thrips has been reported.

Blooms March–April.

213

Phillip Merritt

Arrow Arum

NATIVE

Peltandra virginica

ARACEAE Arum Family

Description. Arrowhead-shaped fleshy leaf blades a foot or more long arise on long stalks from a thick, fibrous root. The flowers are similar to those of other arums, with a leaf-like spathe partly wrapped around a club-like spadix, which bears minute female flowers at its base and male flowers above. Erect in bloom, the flower stalk becomes prostrate in fruit, spilling the numerous black-green berries at the base of the plant.

Habitat. Growing in swamps and shallow waters, the plant survives with special tissue that allows oxygen from its leaves to reach down to the roots. It occurs in the Coastal Plain and Piedmont region of Virginia and ranges from southern Maine to Florida west to Minnesota, Missouri, and Texas; it is naturalized in California and Oregon.

Comments. The genus name comes from Greek *pelta,* "shield," and *andr,* "man," from the shape of the male flowers. Waterfowl consume and help disperse the fruits and seeds. The name Tuckahoe was used by the Algonquin, who ate the plant after prolonged cooking. While the roots are rich in starches, they contain crystals that cause intense burning. Capt. John Smith wrote, "Raw is no better than poison" and "it will prickle and grate the throat extreamly" unless roasted, sliced, and dried in the sun.

Blooms May–June.

214

Skunk Cabbage

NATIVE

Symplocarpus foetidus

ARACEAE Arum Family

Description. One of the few plants blooming in February, Skunk Cabbage when crushed gives off the fetid smell of skunk, hence the species name. The flowers appear before the leaves, in a knob-shaped cluster (spadix) inside a purple-brown and green mottled hood (spathe) 2 to 5 inches long, the spathe generating enough heat to melt surrounding snow. The heat and foul smell attract the first pollinating insects of the year, usually flies. Unfolding later are large oval leaves with blades to 2 feet long. By June the leaves begin to decay and a 3-inch globose fruit mass is formed. By the end of summer scant trace of this perennial is left above ground.

Habitat. Growing in swamps and moist low ground, Skunk Cabbage is widely distributed in Virginia. The range extends from Quebec and Nova Scotia to North Carolina west to Minnesota and Iowa, as well as eastern Asia.

Comments. *Symplocarpus* translates from Greek as "connected fruits," referring to the compound nature of the fruiting spadix. Although the rhizomes are considered toxic, the dried young leaves and rhizomes can be cooked and made into flour.

Blooms January–March.

Common Ragweed

NATIVE

Ambrosia artemisiifolia   ASTERACEAE Aster Family

Description. This very common annual grows 1 to 3 feet or so tall. Leaves are divided into narrow segments with regular lobes. Male flowers are in green, cup-shaped heads in racemes 1 to 6 inches long, producing yellow wind-borne pollen that causes hay fever; the female flowers are in small clusters in axils below the male portion. Numerous seeds are produced, each enclosed in a spiny bur, and may remain viable for 5 years or more.

Habitat. Native to every county in Virginia and throughout the U.S., Common Ragweed grows on cultivated ground, on roadsides, and in fields, dry forests, and waste places. Preferring full sun and average to slightly dry conditions, the plant will grow in clay, gravel, or sand without sufficient nutrients to support other plants. Ragweed also produces chemicals that inhibit the growth of neighboring plants.

Comments. *Ambrosia* is the early Greek name for aromatic plants, the mythic food of the gods; *artemisiifolia* means "like Wormwood, *Artemisia*." While a major cause of hay fever, Common Ragweed is valuable to wildlife. Honeybees collect pollen, and songbirds and gamebirds are attracted to the oil-rich seeds, which often remain above snow cover. However, the bitter taste of the foliage discourages deer.

Blooms August–November.

Large Whorled Pogonia

Small Whorled Pogonia

Left: Ellis Squires   Right: Phillip Merritt

Large Whorled Pogonia   NATIVE

Isotria verticillata   ORCHIDACEAE Orchid Family

Description. This unusual orchid displays its 5 (rarely 6) stalkless leaves in a whorl at the top of a reddish-purple stem. The single stalked flower, which arises from the center of the whorl, has three purple-pigmented sepals that are 2 to 3 times as long as the lip and two side petals. The plant grows in colonies and is seldom more than 12 inches high. The related Small Whorled Pogonia (*I. medeoloides*, right), one of the rarest orchids in Virginia, differs in having no purple pigmentation at all, not even in the stem. Its yellow-green flower has a very short stalk (if any) and the sepals are not much longer than the petals. The stem of both whorled pogonias is fleshy, hollow, and smooth throughout, whereas a lookalike plant, Indian Cucumber Root (*Medeola virginiana*, page 117), has a solid, wiry stem with some fine cottony hairs at the base of the plant.

Habitat. Growing on acidic soils in open to somewhat thickety hard-wood or pine-hardwood stands, Large Whorled Pogonia is widespread throughout Virginia. The range is from southern Maine to Ontario and Michigan and south to northern Florida and east Texas. Efforts are ongoing to protect Virginia populations of the Small Whorled Pogonia.

Comments. *Isotria* is derived from Greek *isos*, meaning "equal," and *tria*, "three," referring to the 3 equal sepals. Pollination is by small solitary bees.

Blooms May–June.

217

Cranefly Orchid

NATIVE

Tipularia discolor   ORCHIDACEAE Orchid Family

Description. In the summer, Cranefly Orchid produces a leafless stalk, to 2 feet tall, of well-spaced greenish-purple flowers, each with a long, slender spur. The flowers are delicate and inconspicuous, often only noticed when a shaft of slanting sunlight highlights what suggests a swarm of small slender insects, such as craneflies (genus *Tipula*). After the flowers disappear, an ovate leaf emerges and is visible all winter. The top of the leaf is gray-green, often mottled, and the underside a bright purple, which is thought to increase the light captured under winter conditions. No leaf is present when the flowers are in bloom.

Habitat. Growing naturally in nearly all counties of Virginia, Cranefly Orchid is found in rich damp woods from Massachusetts to southern Michigan and south to Florida and east Texas.

Comments. The species name *discolor*, "two-colored," refers to the contrasting leaf surfaces. This genus has a complex geological past; its 3 species are located in the Himalayas, Japan, and here in the eastern U.S. Another common name, Crippled Cranefly, refers to the flowers, which incline slightly, facilitating pollination by night-flying moths as pollen-bearing sacs attach to the moth's eyes.

Blooms July–August.

Helen Hamilton

Cleavers

NATIVE

Galium aparine   RUBIACEAE Madder Family

Description. This sprawling annual weed commonly reclines on bushes in thickets, but readily catches onto passersby. Narrow 1- to 3-inch leaves are in whorls of 6 to 8. Tiny, 4-parted white flowers are stalked on axillary branchlets and produce bristly fruits. Other native species of *Galium* differ in leaves and fruits and are perennials with creeping rhizomes.

Habitat. Preferring shady, damp ground, Cleavers is common in woods, thickets, and waste places in every county in Virginia. The plant is nearly cosmopolitan in temperate areas, partly by introduction.

Comments. All parts of this plant, also known as Stickyweed and Goosegrass, are raspy, with hooked hairs that cleave (or cling) to fur and clothing. *Galiums* are also known as Bedstraws, since the pleasant smelling foliage of Yellow Bedstraw *(G. verum)* was used to stuff mattresses in medieval times. The dried, roasted fruits are reported to be the best coffee substitute in North America. Herbal tea of Cleavers has been traditionally used as a folk cancer remedy, as a diuretic, and for bladder and kidney inflammation and kidney stones.

Blooms April–May.

Helen Hamilton

False Nettle

NATIVE

Boehmeria cylindrica URTICACEAE Nettle Family

Description. The leaves and flowers of False Nettle superficially resemble those of the introduced European Stinging Nettle *(Urtica dioica)*, whose stems are covered with bristly, stinging hairs; the stems of False Nettle are smooth. The tiny greenish flowers of this perennial are in head-like clusters arranged along short lateral branches that often bear leaves at their tips. Male and female flowers are usually on separate plants. The fruit is a minute, narrowly-winged achene. False Nettle grows 1 to 3 feet high. The long-stalked leaves are opposite, ovate, and coarsely toothed, with 3 main veins.

Habitat. False Nettle grows in moist or wet soil in shady places such as floodplains and swamps. Found in every county in Virginia, the plant's range is from Quebec and Ontario to Minnesota and south to Florida and New Mexico.

Comments. This plant is a larval host for two common butterflies, the Eastern Comma and the Red Admiral. The genus was named for a professor of botany and anatomy at Wittenberg, Germany, Georg Rudolph Boehmer (1723–1803). An Asian species of the genus is the source of ramie fiber used in rope.

Blooms July–August.

Heartleaf Ginger

NATIVE

Hexastylis virginica   ARISTOLOCHIACEAE Birthwort Family

Description. This species is well named, with evergreen heart-shaped leaves mottled with silvery veining. Leathery and lustrous, the 2- to 3-inch leaves can develop a purple tinge in winter. Each rhizome produces only one leaf each year, held 6 to 8 inches tall, but older leaves persist. Both the roots and leaves have a ginger-like aroma. Bell-shaped, 3-lobed, ½-inch flowers are produced at the base of the plant under the leaves. Brown-purple in color, they are known commonly as Little Brown Jugs.

Habitat. Heartleaf Ginger is restricted to the southeastern states, ranging from Maryland and eastern Kentucky to Georgia and Alabama. Typically growing in acidic soils of moist to dry upland woods, this plant is easy to grow, thriving in partial to deep shade. The plant will form a nice groundcover, providing some green color over the winter.

Comments. The genus *Hexastylis* is named from Greek *hex* for six and *stylus* for style, referring to the six distinct styles on the pistil. The flowers are pollinated by ants and other small insects, which crawl into the flowers and spread the pollen from the open pollen sacs on the anthers to the sticky receptive stigmas.

Blooms April–June.

Common Cattail

NATIVE

Typha latifolia   TYPHACEAE Cattail Family

Description. Slender plants 3 to 10 feet tall in dense colonies are topped by thick, felty-brown clubs. The alternate leaves are sheathing, long and flat, up to an inch wide. In bloom the spike bears an upper section of tiny male flowers. Below, the thicker female section becomes the familiar cylinder of tiny tightly packed fruits bearing slender bristles for transport on the wind. Narrow-leaf Cattail *(T. angustifolia)*, more tolerant of brackish water, has a gap between the male and female portions of the spike. Its leaves are usually ⅜ inch wide or less, but the species overlap in leaf width and hybridize.

Habitat. Growing in freshwater marshes and ditches, Common Cattail is widespread in Virginia; Narrow-leaf Cattail occurs primarily in the Coastal Plain. Both species are nearly cosmopolitan.

Comments. Native Americans found cattails incredibly useful. Poultices were applied to burns, scalds, and inflammations. Flower heads, pollen, stalks, stems, and rhizomes were eaten raw, salted, boiled, ground, dried, or roasted, but twice as many uses were found for fiber and fluff—teepee walls and thatch, mats, bedding, clothing, ties for sandals, storage bags, and basketry. Cattails have been dubbed "the supermarket of the swamps."

Blooms May–July.

Helen Hamilton

American Beach Grass NATIVE

Ammophila breviligulata POACEAE Grass Family

Description. This important sand-binder is a perennial plant growing to 5 feet tall. Forming around the base of the plant and extending upward, the leaves are long, narrow, and pointed. The flowers are compacted into a cylindrical spikelike panicle, which in late summer turns from green to light gray as the seeds form.

Habitat. American Beach Grass occurs in Virginia only in the coastal counties. The plant is common on beach sands and dunes of the ocean and bay shores from Newfoundland to North Carolina. Often planted to stabilize dunes, this grass can withstand burial by shifting sands, sending up another vertical stem from underground horizontal stems. On very high dunes the distance from the plant on the top of the dune to the tip of the main root below may be 40 feet or more. In between, there may be remnants of plants that have been buried over the years.

Comments. The name comes from Greek *ammos*, "sand," and *philein*, "to love"; *breviligulata* because the ligules (thin structures on the inside of the leaf) are short.

Blooms August–September.

Bushy Bluestem NATIVE

Andropogon glomeratus   POACEAE Grass Family

Description. This perennial grass looks like a small upturned broom, with the flowers and seed heads in tight clusters covered with many soft silky hairs. Bushy Bluestem grows about 4 feet tall, usually in clumps, the stems branching at the tips. The stem and leaves have a bluish cast early in the season, becoming tan later and a deep orange-red in the fall and winter.

Habitat. Bushy Bluestem is frequent in low moist areas in full sun such as roadside ditches, meadows, and grassland swales. The plant is common in the eastern counties of Virginia and scattered elsewhere in the state. The range extends from the West Indies and Central America north to California, Arkansas, and Virginia and along the Coastal Plain to Massachusetts.

Comments. The genus name is composed of Greek *aner (andr)*, "man," and *pogon*, "beard." The Cherokee have used this species as a ceremonial medicine and a dermatological aid and to make a yellow dye. The seeds are eaten by birds and small mammals, and the sturdy stems provide nesting material for birds and good cover for small animals. Bluestem grasses are larval hosts for skipper and satyr butterflies. All grasses are highly deer resistant.

Blooms September–October.

224

Splitbeard Bluestem

NATIVE

Andropogon ternarius POACEAE Grass Family

Description. This is a distinctive grass in the fall, with paired, silvery-white seed tufts at the ends of the stems. The fluffy seed heads catch the sun and often persist into winter. Growing in clumps, Splitbeard Bluestem has 1- to 4-foot stems. Narrow, ribbon-like leaves toward the base of the plant are glaucous and blue-green in the summer, turning copper, red, and bronze in the fall.

Habitat. Preferring hot dry sites with poor soil but good drainage, Splitbeard Bluestem grows in southeastern counties of Virginia. This plant is common in dry places, thin woods, pinelands, old fields, meadows, and on roadsides throughout the southeastern U.S. from Delaware to Kentucky and southern Missouri south to Florida and Texas.

Comments. This is a stunning grass for a meadow or wildflower border with the sun back-lighting masses of the V-shaped seed tufts. Juncos and Chipping Sparrows eat the seeds. Splitbeard Bluestem is a host plant for the Wood Nymph butterfly, whose caterpillars feed on the foliage.

Blooms September–October.

Helen Hamilton

Sweet Vernal Grass

Anthoxanthum odoratum POACEAE Grass Family

Description. Sweet Vernal Grass is distinguished by 12- to 18-inch flowering stems bearing dense, soft tufts of flowers to 6 inches long. A short-lived perennial grass of early spring, it has stems that are first green and then tan; all foliage will disappear by midsummer. The pollen from the dangling anthers is known to be a major cause of spring hay fever.

Habitat. Found in every county in Virginia, Sweet Vernal Grass was introduced to North America from Europe in the late 1700s as a meadow grass and has since spread from cultivation. Considered a weed, this is a familiar grass of suburban areas. It occurs on poorer soils of dry fields, lawns, meadows, roadsides, and waste places. The North American range is from Newfoundland to Georgia and west to Michigan, Illinois, and Louisiana.

Comments. The genus name *Anthoxanthum* is derived from Greek *anthos*, meaning "flower," and *xanthos*, meaning "yellow," alluding to the yellow inflorescence. When the leaves are crushed, they release a sweet vanilla-like odor. The sweetness comes from a chemical that is converted into coumarin when the hay becomes moldy, causing a bleeding disease in cattle.

Blooms April–July.

226

Switch Cane

NATIVE

Arundinaria tecta   POACEAE Grass Family

Description. This perennial is a North American member of the Bamboo tribe of grasses and resembles introduced Asian bamboos. Growing to 6 feet tall, Switch Cane has slender, woody, hollow stems and long flat leaves forming fanlike clusters. It grows to 6 feet and flowers probably every 3 to 4 years.

Habitat. Switch Cane grows in swampy woods and wetlands in Virginia's Coastal Plain, with a few records in the Piedmont region. This grass is endemic to the southeastern Coastal Plain, occurring only from eastern Maryland to Florida and southern Alabama. Switch Cane has been considered a subspecies of the much larger River Cane *(A. gigantea)*, a species found in southwestern Virginia and ranging into the lower Mississippi River basin (wrongly attributed to eastern Virginia).

Comments. Populations of this grass were much reduced by the foraging of free-range livestock in the 18th and 19th centuries and by fire suppression later. Canebrakes, large areas dominated by cane, are described in many historical accounts and apparently occupied large parts of the Coastal Plain, also occurring in the Piedmont and low mountains. Native Americans used the canes for many purposes such as housing materials, fishing poles, basketry, and medicines.

Blooms April–July.

Helen Hamilton

Dune Sandspur

NATIVE

Cenchrus tribuloides   POACEAE Grass Family

Description. This is a much-branched trailing annual plant with stout stems about 12 inches tall. Leathery and rough to the touch, the leaf blades are less than ½ inch across and fold inward, appearing round. Flowers are enclosed in a green bur that turns brown in the fall; the bur is armed with strong, barbed spines that are quite painful when lodged in the skin. These are particularly troublesome to animals, often lodging between the toes of dogs. Other species of *Cenchrus* are recognized by differences in the spines and leaf blades.

Habitat. Dune Sandspur grows in sandy fields, woods, and coastal sands. This is the most common species of this genus that visitors encounter in coastal areas. The range is from southern New York to Florida and Texas, and rarely tropical America.

Comments. Despite its formidable burs, Sandspur does have redeeming qualities as a sand binder. The stems produce roots while lying flat, thereby securing the plant; the low profile and rooted stems reduce wind abrasion and increase water uptake.

Blooms August–October.

228

River Oats

Spikegrass

River Oats   NATIVE

Chasmanthium latifolium   POACEAE Grass Family

Description. River Oats is easily identified from the flat, drooping spike-lets hanging in terminal clusters on thread-like pedicels from slightly arching stems. The 5- to 9-inch-long bright-green leaves become tan in the winter. This clump-forming, upright ornamental grass grows 2 to 5 feet tall and self-seeds aggressively. Spikegrass (*C. laxum*, lower photo) is a perennial woodland grass to 4 feet tall on thin, wand-like stems, often bent horizontal, lined at regular intervals with small spikelets.

Habitat. Widespread in Virginia in moist open woods and on stream-banks, River Oats prefers some shade and well-drained, moist, fertile soils. The range is from New Jersey to Georgia and Florida west to Illinois, Kansas, and Texas. Spikegrass grows in extensive drifts in moist pine woods, meadows, and swamps in the Coastal Plain and Piedmont, ranging from Long Island, Kentucky, and Missouri to Florida and Texas.

Comments. River Oats (formerly known as *Uniola latifolia*) was once thought to be a close relative of the coastal, sand-binding Sea Oats (*Uniola paniculata*); both have superficially similar large, attractive, flat-tened spikelets. *Chasmanthium* derives from the Greek *chasme*, "gap-ing," and *anthus*, "flower," as the parts open to expose the mature grain. *Latifolium* means "broad-leaved."

Blooms June–October.

Helen Hamilton

Orchard Grass

Dactylis glomerata   POACEAE Grass Family

Description. A cool-season perennial, Orchard Grass blooms in early spring, its florets in irregular rounded clusters. This grass grows in dense tufts to 3 feet tall and has deep bluish-green stems and leaves. With a deep root system, the plant is useful for preventing soil erosion.

Habitat. Orchard Grass was introduced into this country from Europe as a forage grass in the late 1700s. It was first cultivated in Virginia and is now found in every county in Virginia and throughout North America. This grass will grow in any soil type, acidic or basic, sandy or clay, in full sun or part shade. Occurring along roadsides, at woodland edges, and in pastures and fields, when mowed it will grow back vigorously and flower again.

Comments. Orchard Grass is still grown today for hay, and its pollen is a major cause of spring hay fever. The genus name is from Greek *dactylos* meaning "finger"; *glomerata* means "clustered," referring to the appearance of the groups of florets.

Blooms May–October.

230

Poverty Oatgrass

NATIVE

Danthonia spicata   POACEAE Grass Family

Description. This clump-forming perennial is distinctive, with wiry tufts of curly basal leaves and nearly leafless stems. Old basal leaves persist throughout the year, tan-colored, more curved and inrolled. Small flowers develop on stalks 1 foot tall with 2 to 3 short and straight alternate leaves. The leaves of a related species, Silky Oatgrass *(D. sericea)*, are longer and parts of the plant are silky-hairy.

Habitat. Poverty Oatgrass prefers dry, stony soils in sun or light shade. The grass is widespread in Virginia and across the U.S. and southern Canada. Silky Oatgrass grows in dry sandy soil and pine woods, chiefly on the Coastal Plain, extending from Massachusetts and southern New Jersey to Kentucky and south to Florida and Louisiana.

Comments. The genus was named in 1805 for French botanist Etienne Danthoine. *Spicata* means "with spikes" and *sericea*, "silky." Because of its dense tufts of curly basal leaves, Poverty Oatgrass is relatively easy to identify, even when not in bloom.

Blooms May–July.

Virginia Wild Rye   Bottlebrush Grass

Left: Helen Hamilton   Right: Phillip Merritt

Virginia Wild Rye

NATIVE

Elymus virginicus

POACEAE Grass Family

Description. Growing to 4 feet tall, the stiff, upright stems of Virginia Wild Rye carry a single floral spike 2 to 6 inches long densely covered with awned spikelets. A related perennial, Bottlebrush Grass (*E. hystrix*, right), is well named because the blooming, awned spikelets lined up on the stem look exactly like a laboratory bottle brush waiting to clean a test tube. The alternate leaves of both species are medium to dark green, hairless, and rather floppy.

Habitat. Virginia Wild Rye grows in moist woods, meadows, and thickets, and on shores of freshwater marshes, ranging from Newfoundland west to Alberta and south to Florida and Arizona. Bottlebrush Grass occurs in dry or moist woodlands in open shade and ranges from Nova Scotia to North Dakota and south to Georgia, Tennessee, and Oklahoma. Both species are found in every county in Virginia.

Comments. The genus name comes from Greek *elyo*, "rolled up," referring to the coverings over the grain. The species name of Bottlebrush Grass comes from the Greek word *hystrix*, "hedgehog," referring to the resemblance of the seedhead bristles to hedgehog quills. A good forage grass, species of *Elymus* have been used by Native Americans for medicinal purposes, food, fiber, and fodder.

Blooms June–October.

232

Purple Lovegrass

NATIVE

Eragrostis spectabilis

POACEAE Grass Family

Description. This is an attractive ornamental grass with very diffuse clusters of fine reddish-purple spikelets on stiff pedicels. In late summer and early fall they turn tan, and the whole panicle eventually breaks away and tumbles before the wind, distributing seeds along the way. The plants also spread by stems rooting along the ground at the nodes. The leaves are firm, flat, and tapering and less than an inch wide. Both the flowering stems and leaves of this perennial grass can reach 2 feet tall.

Habitat. Purple Lovegrass is common in loose sands, stable dune areas, fencerows, fields, and dry pinelands. This plant grows best on moist, sandy soil in full sun or in well-drained open fields. Native to the eastern and central U.S. from Maine to North Dakota and south to Florida and Texas, Purple Lovegrass grows in nearly every county in Virginia.

Comments. The genus name *Eragrostis* possibly comes from Greek *Eros*, the god of love, and *agrostis*, "a grass," since some Old World species were long known as lovegrass; *spectabilis* means "spectacular."

Blooms August–October.

Helen Hamilton

Velvet Grass

INTRODUCED

Holcus lanatus   POACEAE Grass Family

Description. This perennial grass is well named, having velvety stems and leaves with soft hairs all over. Stiff, erect stems rise to 3 feet tall with pale green, flat, and relatively wide leaves. The inflorescence is a purplish panicle, narrow and drooping at first, the spikelets dense in narrowly ovoid clusters.

Habitat. Velvet Grass is common in pastures and hedgerows, along roadsides, and in meadows in moist soil. A native of Europe, the plant is now well established throughout the U.S. and in most other temperate areas, and in nearly every county of Virginia. An aggressive weed, the plant was brought into this country in the 1800s for forage, but cattle were never fond of it; ingestion is reported to inflame the mucous membranes of the mouth. Where abundant, this grass can cause hay fever.

Comments. The genus name was used by Pliny for a type of grass, from Greek *holcus*, meaning "attractive." *Lanatus* is Latin for "woolly."

Blooms May–October.

Perennial Rye Grass INTRODUCED

Lolium perenne   POACEAE Grass Family

Description. Perennial Rye Grass is a short-lived perennial with slender stems growing to 3 feet tall. Flowering spikes are slender, straight or slightly curved, and about an inch long. The rachis is somewhat flexible, bearing 5 to 37 spikelets lying against its concavities. The dark-green leaves are folded lengthwise when in bud form.

Habitat. A native of Europe, this grass has been cultivated in meadows and lawns and occasionally escapes to roadsides and waste places. The plant grows in any soil and requires full sun and moist soil, but it can tolerate drought. It is found throughout the U.S. and Canada and in most counties of Virginia; it can be invasive.

Comments. Perennial Rye Grass is an important pasture and forage plant and is used in many pasture seed mixes. It has been casually used in folk remedies for cancer, diarrhea, hemorrhage, and malaria. In the South, rye grasses are used as temporary turfgrasses for overseeding dormant warm-season grasses. They can provide a green cover during the winter, preventing erosion on new lawns until the permanent grass can be established.

Blooms April–July.

Helen Hamilton

Asian Stiltgrass

Microstegium vimineum

POACEAE Grass Family

Description. Asian Stiltgrass is a low, straggling annual, growing in massive drifts. Pale-green leaves are lance-shaped and to 4 inches long with a shiny midrib. Spreading by seed germination in the spring, it also roots at the joints along the lower stem during the growing season. In late summer, inconspicuous seeds develop at branch tips and can remain viable in the seed bank for up to 7 years.

Habitat. A native of Asia from India to Japan, this extremely invasive plant thrives in moist, often shaded habitats such as floodplains, streambanks, moist uplands, thickets, and shaded clearings. First documented in Tennessee around 1919, Asian Stiltgrass may have been accidentally introduced as packing material for porcelain. Now common in every county in Virginia, the plant has spread throughout the eastern U.S. and Texas.

Comments. Asian Stiltgrass forms extensive patches overwhelming and eliminating other herbaceous plants. Avoiding this plant, deer will feed on native plant species instead, thus facilitating its invasion. Almost impossible to eradicate given its long-lived seeds, it has shallow roots, and hand-pulling or mowing before seeds are produced is helpful.

Blooms August–October.

Switchgrass

Beaked Panicgrass

Helen Hamilton

Switchgrass

NATIVE

Panicum virgatum   POACEAE Grass Family

Description. This perennial is easily recognized by 6-foot-tall, erect to arching stems, open panicle, and long, tapering leaves. Switchgrass grows in clumps that expand over several years. With deep, wide roots, this is a very important forage grass of the tallgrass prairies. Beaked Panicgrass (*P. anceps*, right) grows to 3 feet with a spreading panicle. The spikelets are distinctive from those of other Panicums—curved like a bird's beak, away from the stalk.

Habitat. Switchgrass grows along the edges of ponds and marshes, in wet pinelands, and on swales, prairies, dunes, and shores. In Virginia the plant is found mostly in the eastern counties; it is widely distributed over most of the U.S. and Canada. Beaked Panicgrass grows best in partial shade in sandy soil, occurring throughout all regions of Virginia.

Comments. The seeds of these grasses are eaten by upland birds, waterfowl, and cattle. Switchgrass has become of major interest as a source of biofuels. Beaked Panicgrass is used for the revegetation of surfaces such as mined land, logging roads and sites, and other disturbed areas. The genus name may come from Latin *panus*, "an ear of millet"; *virgatum* means "wand-like."

Blooms June–October.

Dallis Grass

Florida Paspalum

Helen Hamilton

Dallis Grass INTRODUCED

Paspalum dilatatum   POACEAE Grass Family

Description. Dallis Grass grows in sprawling tufts up to 3 feet tall. Flat, hemispheric spikelets fringed with long silky hairs line one side of the rachis. The linear leaves are folded and taper to an inrolled point. Often growing to 6 feet tall, native Florida Paspalum (*P. floridanum,* right) is distinctive for its large seeds (¼ inch long), hard and roundish and somewhat resembling domestic corn, in erect or drooping spikes well above the leaves.

Habitat. Dallis grass is very weedy and can be expected almost anywhere in the open, most frequently along roadsides, in lawns and fields, and in moist places. A native of South America, it has been cultivated and has widely escaped in the southern U.S., extending north to New Jersey, Kentucky, and California. Both grasses occur in eastern and central Virginia.

Comments. The genus name probably comes from Greek *paspalos,* "millet" or "meal." This was a valuable pasture plant for Native Americans. For livestock, the young leaves are palatable and nutritious, but *Paspalums,* like some other grasses, may become infected with deadly ergot fungi.

Blooms May–October.

238

Left: Jan Newton   Right: Phillip Merritt

Common Reed   INTRODUCED INVASIVE/NATIVE

Phragmites australis ssp. *australis*   POACEAE Grass Family

Description. With stout stems to 12 feet tall, this perennial forms extensive stands from underground stems. The inflorescence is a dense tawny to purplish feathery panicle becoming straw-colored with age. Inch-wide leaf blades are long and flat with a bluish tinge. A native subspecies, P. *australis* ssp. *americanus*, is difficult to distinguish from the introduced plant; its leaf-sheaths disintegrate with age, exposing the smooth shiny stems.

Habitat. Common in fresh marshes, swamps, and wet shores, this grass is nearly cosmopolitan. It is tolerant of salt, thrives in brackish soils, and occurs in the eastern counties in Virginia. The native subspecies is less frequent here but appears to be native on all continents except Antarctica.

Comments. *Phragmites* is Greek for "growing in hedges," apparently from the plant's hedge-like growth along ditches. The introduced subspecies may have arrived as ballast in the late 18th century. It quickly displaces Wild Rice, cattails, and even Wax Myrtle. Fragments 3000 to 4000 years old of the native subspecies suggest its household use by Native Americans. Common Reed has had numerous uses almost everywhere, past and present.

Blooms September–October.

239

Helen Hamilton

Golden Bamboo

Phyllostachys aurea

INTRODUCED INVASIVE

POACEAE Grass Family

Description. Golden Bamboo is a highly invasive, woody, perennial, reed-like plant that can reach 25 feet in height. Lance-shaped leaves to 1 inch wide grow to 5 inches long. Flowering is rare and unpredictable, occurring once every 15 to 20 years. Forming dense thickets, this grass quickly displaces native species.

Habitat. Golden Bamboo is native to China and was introduced into the U.S. before 1870. The plant grows in semi-shade in any soil, usually moist, but can tolerate drought. It is commonly found around old homesites and in other landscaping.

Comments. *Phyllum* is Greek for "a leaf," and *stachys*, "a spike," from the leafy spikelets; *aurea* means "golden." Quickly spreading by rhizomes and producing dense, tall canes, Golden Bamboo has been used for screening, fencing, and erosion control, but its aggressive growth habit dominates the landscape and chokes all other vegetation. The rhizomes will grow under and through asphalt and concrete. Effective control is difficult—cutting all green growth will eventually starve the rhizomes; mature canes should be cut to the ground and immediately painted with an herbicide. Young shoots are reported as very palatable; mature canes make excellent fishing poles.

Blooming is infrequent and not predictable.

Helen Hamilton

Annual Bluegrass

Poa annua   POACEAE Grass Family

Description. This bluegrass is low and sprawling, usually about 12 inches wide, and often forms dense mats. Leaves are bright green, the tip shaped like the bow of a boat. The panicle of spikelets is not more than 4 inches long and is large relative to the short stature (under a foot) of the plant. Each spikelet has 3 to 8 bright green to purplish flowers. Reproducing by seed, Annual Bluegrass can have several generations in a season. These plants die in late spring, leaving light-colored mats and becoming unsightly and troublesome in lawns. Kentucky Bluegrass *(P. pratensis)* is an introduced perennial commonly used as a lawn grass, growing 1 to 3 feet tall uncut.

Habitat. Native to Eurasia, Annual Bluegrass is a common plant of lawns, swales, paths, roadsides, waste places, parking lots, crevices of sidewalks, and shrub and flower plantings. The grass occurs in every county in Virginia and is abundant throughout the contiguous U.S. and north to Labrador and Alaska. From Europe, Kentucky Bluegrass may be native in Canada.

Comments. The genus name is from Greek *poa*, meaning "grass" or "fodder."

Blooms April–May.

241

Helen Hamilton

Sugarcane Plumegrass

NATIVE

Saccharum giganteum   POACEAE Grass Family

Description. This is one of the tallest grasses, growing to 12 feet on reedlike stems, often forming clumps or large colonies. Leaf blades are long and flat, to 1 inch wide and 2 feet long. At the base of the leaf blade, the ligule is a collar with fringing hairs. The inflorescence is a very large, dense panicle to 18 inches long and 5 inches wide which looks different as it ages, pink to white, becoming purple to bronze in the fall. The plume is full of long-haired paired spikelets with bristles (awns) to 1 inch long. Just below the flower head the stem is silky-hairy. Another native, Short-beard Plumegrass *(S. brevibarbe* var. *contortus)*, is shorter, to 6 feet tall, with smooth stems.

Habitat. Growing in moist ground, marshes, ditches, and low woods, Sugarcane Plumegrass occurs in the Coastal Plain and Piedmont counties in Virginia. The range is from New Jersey to Kentucky and Arkansas and south to Florida and Texas.

Comments. The name is derived from Greek *sakharon*, meaning "sugar." This grass is a member of the same genus as sugar cane. It may have been the dominant grassland plant in the southeast U.S. before humans arrived.

Blooms September–October.

Little Bluestem

NATIVE

Schizachyrium scoparium   POACEAE Grass Family

Description. Little Bluestem is an important perennial grass, growing to 5 feet with wiry flowering branches intermingling with the leaves. Blue-green only when the shoots first come up in the early summer, the leaves and flowering stalks become a rich mixture of tan, brown, and wine-red through the fall and winter. The bent awns on the mature spikelets borne in clusters lining the branches are a distinguishing feature. Broomsedge *(Andropogon virginicus)* has a similar appearance, with silvery flower clusters on the branches and reddish stems during the winter, but the awns on its mature spikelets are not bent.

Habitat. These grasses grow in dry soil, old fields, open pine woods, and brackish bayside meadows. One of the dominant species of the tallgrass prairies, Little Bluestem is widespread over most of the U.S. and Canada. Broomsedge, often an indicator of poor soils, ranges through the eastern and central U.S.; it is introduced in California and invasive in Hawaii.

Comments. An excellent forage grass, Little Bluestem was once the most abundant species in the American tall and mixed-grass prairie region. Since most of the prairies have been destroyed, it is most familiar in old fields in the Northeast and in prairie remnants.

Blooms August–October.

Nodding Foxtail   Giant Foxtail

Helen Hamilton

Nodding Foxtail

INTRODUCED

Setaria faberi   POACEAE Grass Family

Description. Growing to 6 feet, this annual grass is easily recognized by the drooping, bristly inflorescence (to 8 inches) topping a long stalk; there are 1 to 3 bristles below each spikelet. Long slender leaves are an inch wide and rough on both sides. The flowering spikes of the introduced Green Foxtail *(S. viridis)* are a pale green, shorter, and erect, not drooping. The native Giant Foxtail (*S. magna*, right) grows to 12 feet tall with a drooping inflorescence up to 2 feet long.

Habitat. Nodding Foxtail was introduced into the U.S. from East Asia during the 1920s, probably in contaminated shipments of grain, and is now widespread in the eastern and central U.S. This grass grows in fields and waste places in nearly every county in Virginia. Green Foxtail is native to Eurasia and common in fields and disturbed areas. Giant Foxtail is found only in the coastal counties of Virginia, growing in brackish marshes from New Jersey to Florida and Texas, introduced from south of the U.S.

Comments. The genus name *Setaria* is from *seta* for "bristle" and the species *faberi* is for Ernst Faber (1839–1899), who discovered the species in China. Producing many seeds, these plants are a valuable food source for birds.

Blooms July–October.

Knotroot Foxtail

Yellow Foxtail

Helen Hamilton

Knotroot Foxtail

NATIVE

Setaria parviflora (S. geniculata)   POACEAE Grass Family

Description. This erect perennial grass grows to 3 feet tall from short, knotty rhizomes. Stems are often bent at the base, then ascending. Purplish leaves are up to 8 inches long, tapering and mostly flat. The inflorescence is dense and spikelike, 1 to 4 inches long and less than ½-inch wide, with 4 to 12 yellow to purple bristles below each spikelet. An introduced species, Yellow Foxtail (*S. pumila*, lower photo) is an annual, often tufted, the stems erect from fibrous roots, leaves yellowish green. The spikelets are longer, with up to 20 yellowish bristles.

Habitat. Knotroot Foxtail is common in brackish marshes and on moist to dry ground and waste places. It is scattered across Virginia and ranges from tropical North America north to California, Texas, Iowa, West Virginia, and Massachusetts. Yellow Foxtail is a native of Europe, now a cosmopolitan weed abundant through the U.S. and Canada and in most counties in Virginia. It grows in dry to wet places in the open—roadsides, fields, around buildings, and shrub borders.

Comments. The seeds of foxtails are an important source of food for wildlife. Livestock sometimes injure their mouths consuming the barbed bristles.

Blooms May–October.

245

Yellow Indian Grass

NATIVE

Sorghastrum nutans   POACEAE Grass Family

Description. Growing 2 to 8 feet tall and topped by large plume-like, golden-brown spikelets, Yellow Indian Grass is particularly attractive in the fall, when the flowers produce dangling yellow stamens. The leaves are slender, ½ inch wide and 2 feet long, and blue-green, turning orange-yellow to purple in the fall. Slender Indian Grass *(S. elliottii)* has narrower leaves, the panicle is less hairy, and the awns are noticeably bent.

Habitat. Widespread in Virginia and over most of the U.S. and Canada, Yellow Indian Grass grows in limestone soils, in open woods, on road banks, and in fields. It is easily grown in average, well-drained soils in full sun and does well in poor, dry, and infertile soils. Slender Indian Grass occurs chiefly on the Coastal Plain from Maryland to Florida and Texas and inland to Tennessee and Arkansas.

Comments. Along with Big Bluestem, Little Bluestem, and Switchgrass, Yellow Indian Grass is one of the dominant grasses of the tallgrass prairie. Seeds are relished by birds and small mammals, and because the plant is tall and erect over the winter, it provides good cover for many kinds of birds and animals. Yellow Indian Grass is a larval host plant for the Pepper and Salt Skipper butterfly.

Blooms September–November.

Saltmarsh Cordgrass

NATIVE

Spartina alterniflora   POACEAE Grass Family

Description. This erect perennial grows to 8 feet tall on stout hollow stems often soft and spongy at the base. Leaf blades are flat and smooth on the edges, up to 16 inches long, and tapering to a long point with an inwardly rolled tip. The flowers appear alternately on the ends of the stems in narrow rows, whitish green in bloom and tan in fruit. Salt crystals can often be seen on the leaves during the growing season. This plant and other salt marsh species can grow in high saline conditions by excreting the salt taken up by the roots.

Habitat. Saltmarsh Cordgrass is the dominant plant of salt marshes on the Atlantic Coast, comprising 90 percent of these marshes. An extremely hardy plant, it tolerates tidal saltwater inundation and storm-lashed waters. Found only in the coastal areas in Virginia, the range is from Quebec and Newfoundland to Florida and Texas, but where introduced in areas along the Pacific Coast of the U.S. it is considered invasive.

Comments. Because of its tenaciousness, Saltmarsh Cordgrass is valued for its ability to inhibit erosion. Waterfront property owners who plant this grass within the intertidal zone of their shorelines have a fringing marsh as a buffer to wave action.

Blooms August–October.

Giant Cordgrass

NATIVE

Spartina cynosuroides   POACEAE Grass Family

Description. Giant Cordgrass grows to 10 feet tall with inch-thick hollow stems. The elongate leaves are arranged on the stem in overlapping sheaths, the leaves coming off at different angles. Along the margins of the leaves are minute upturned teeth, which can scratch or cut the skin. The flowers are terminal, the spikelets densely crowded on long, finger-like stalks, turning from green to tan when in seed. This perennial propagates both by seed and underground stems (rhizomes).

Habitat. This grass grows only in the coastal counties of Virginia. Common in brackish and freshwater tidal marshes, often standing in water, it ranges on the coast from Massachusetts to Florida and Texas.

Comments. *Cynosuroides* means "like *Cynosurus*," Dogtail Grass. This is the largest of the *Spartina* marsh grasses, frequently growing in dense, pure stands along tidal rivers that may extend 50 miles or more inland from the Atlantic. It often forms a tall border along the marsh/upland edge of salt marshes. Giant Cordgrass is frequently used by duck hunters as camouflage for duck blinds. The long, stout rhizomes are a favorite food for geese, who dig them out. Muskrats use the foliage and stems for lodge construction.

Blooms June–September.

248

Phillip Merritt

Saltmeadow Cordgrass NATIVE

Spartina patens POACEAE Grass Family

Description. Saltmeadow Cordgrass is a fine, wiry, erect or spreading perennial grass, usually 1 to 3 feet tall. The base of the stem is weak and has a tendency to bend when stressed by winds or tides, producing the characteristic cowlicks or swirls occurring in large salt marsh meadows. The leaves are very narrow and arranged in two ranks around the stem, the edges rolled inward so the blade appears round. The brown inflorescence is usually composed of 3 to 6 spikes alternately arranged at the ends of the stems.

Habitat. This grass is found only in eastern counties of Virginia. It is common in salt and brackish marshes, on beaches, and in coastal meadows from Quebec to Florida and Texas, and in saline situations inland from New York to Michigan.

Comments. The genus name is derived from Greek *spartine*, "a cord"; *patens* means "spreading." Saltmeadow Cordgrass is an important component of the rich salt marsh ecosystem; the detritus produced by this plant and others adds organic material to the marsh. Young shoots have no trouble growing up through the thatch of narrow stems in the spring. The principal source of eastern salt hay, it is grazed or harvested as a forage crop for cattle in many marshes along the East Coast.

Blooms June–September.

Helen Hamilton

Purpletop

NATIVE

Tridens flavus   POACEAE Grass Family

Description. Purpletop is easily recognized in late summer by its loose, open, purple spikelets in a distinctive weeping form. This slender perennial grows to 4 feet tall, the upper stem branched with spikelets covered by a waxy, greasy substance, and an alternate name is Grease Grass. The large purple seeds are widely spaced on thin branches of the panicle. Somewhat flattened leaves are long, ½ inch wide, and usually glabrous with a hairy sheath. The upper surface and margins of the leaf blade are rough to the touch.

Habitat. Purpletop is common along roadsides, in fields, and on edges of woods. Occurring in every county in Virginia, it ranges from Massachusetts, southern Michigan, and Nebraska south to Florida and Texas.

Comments. The genus name is from Latin *tridens*, "three-toothed," referring to the 3-nerved lemma (a spikelet part); *flavus* means "pale yellow." Birds eat the seeds, and this robust grass provides significant cover for wildlife; it is also grazed by livestock. Purpletop is the larval host for 4 species of butterflies, including the Common Wood-nymph.

Blooms July–October.

Gamagrass

Tripsacum dactyloides   POACEAE Grass Family

Description. This perennial grass grows 3 to 8 feet tall in clusters or colonies. Leaves are to an inch wide, somewhat resembling those of domestic corn. At the end of the major stems, flower spikes bear tan male flowers above the fuzzy purple female flowers. The male portion of the spike resembles the tassel of corn plants and drops off after shedding pollen. The female flowers and grains develop into bony beadlike joints.

Habitat. Gamagrass is found in moist places such as ditches, moist river banks, and the edges of marshes and woods. Occurring in eastern and central Virginia, this important species of moist and wetland areas in the Great Plains is generally seen in disturbed habitats. The range is from Massachusetts to Michigan and Nebraska and southward to the tropics.

Comments. *Tripsacum* may derive from Greek *tribein*, "to rub," and refer to the polished spikes; *dactyloides* means "finger-like." The separated male and female flowers and the grains suggest a relationship to domestic corn *(Zea mays)*, and artificial hybrids can be made between *Zea* and *Tripsacum*. Gamagrass is prized for both hay and grazing.

Blooms June–November.

Phillip Merritt

Wild Rice

Zizania aquatica

POACEAE Grass Family

Description. Often just offshore in marshes, Wild Rice is recognizable by its large open cluster of spikelets divided into two parts. The male flowers hang from the spreading lower branches, while the females are erect on the stiff, broomlike upper branches. This annual grows up to 12 feet tall on stout stems. Leaves are to 2 inches wide and 3 feet long. Southern Wild Rice *(Zizaniopsis miliacea)* is perennial from rhizomes; the male and female flowers share the same branches.

Habitat. In Virginia, Wild Rice grows only in coastal counties in fresh and slightly brackish marshes and stream borders. The range extends from Quebec down the coastal states to Florida and Louisiana and irregularly inland to the Midwest. Southern Wild Rice is widespread in tidal freshwaters of the Coastal Plain.

Comments. Stands of Wild Rice are harvested repeatedly since the seeds do not mature simultaneously and readily shatter from the plant. Native Americans used canoes, pulling the stalks into the boat and gently beating them to release mature kernels. A famous Indian dish was tassimanonny—boiled wild rice, corn, and fish. A staple food for wildlife, Wild Rice is now marketed as a specialty high in protein and low in fat.

Blooms May–October.

Helen Hamilton

Fringed Sedge

NATIVE

Carex crinita   CYPERACEAE Sedge Family

Description. Often confused with grasses, sedges usually have 3-angled stems with leaves in 3 ranks. Species recognition can be very difficult, involving how the female and male flowers are arranged and their characters. More than 184 species and varieties of *Carex* are known from Virginia. One example is Fringed Sedge, the male flowers in one (usually) to three elongate spikes (the rightmost of four in the photo) that are separate from and located on the stem above spikes with female flowers. The spikes with female flowers (the middle three in the photo) are elongate and drooping, with a bristly appearance due to the long awns on the scales under each female flower. Bright-green leaves are taller than the flowering spikes.

Habitat. Fringed Sedge occurs in every county in Virginia and throughout the eastern and central U.S. and Canada. Many sedges prefer wet or boggy soil and are found in moist woods, swamps, marshes, and ditches.

Comments. Sedges can form an intermediate step between mud and dry land by spreading their rhizomes and acting as a landfill, allowing other vegetation to grow. Many can be planted as ornamentals in ordinary garden soil, their interesting spikes providing attractive contrast.

Blooms June–August.

253

Right: Helen Hamilton   Left: Phillip Merritt

Soft Rush

NATIVE

Juncus effusus   JUNCACEAE Rush Family

Description. Grass-like but not a grass, this erect perennial herb grows to 3 feet tall, forming dense clumps. The stems are stout, round, and unbranched, remaining greenish through winter. A pointed bract appearing as a continuation of the culm extends above the inflorescence; this bract is less hardened or bristly than in Black Needle Rush (*J. roemerianus*, page 255), thus the common name describing a "soft" rush. There are no apparent leaves, and the flowers appear in an inconspicuous greenish-brown cluster projecting from one side of the upper third of the stem. The flowers are small and scaly but more conventional than those of grasses, as the parts are in threes and the fruit is a capsule with many minute seeds.

Habitat. Native to every county in Virginia, Soft Rush grows in wet meadows, freshwater marshes, and shrubby swamps. The plant is nearly cosmopolitan in temperate regions, growing best in moist to wet soils in full sun or light shade. In the home garden it makes a nice addition to damp spots, the spiky stems contrasting with broad-leaved perennials.

Comments. Muskrats feed on the rootstocks. Jamestown colonists opened the stems to extract the pith, a continuous column of white cells, which they soaked in animal fat and used for candle wicks.

Blooms June–September.

Phillip Merritt

Black Needle Rush

Juncus roemerianus　　　　　　　JUNCACEAE Rush Family

Description. This perennial grasslike plant grows to 6 feet tall. The stems are dark green (blackish from a distance), stiff and with a sharp point on the terminal bract. There are no apparent leaves. The flowers are inconspicuous, green or light brown, borne in clusters appearing to be lateral from above the middle of the stem. Grayish dead stems are evident in large masses of these plants.

Habitat. Black Needle Rush grows in coastal tidal salt marshes, forming dense, pure stands at and above mean high tide. It is found in the coastal counties of Virginia and in similar habitats from southern New Jersey to Florida and Texas.

Comments. Juncus comes from *iuncus*, "rush," derived from *iungere*, "to bind or join," from the use of the stems in tying. The species was named for Karl von Roemer (1818–1891), geologist and Texas explorer. Black Needle Rush is one of the most important plants in salt marshes. In this habitat it is easily recognized as masses of dark green, with hard, needle-tipped leaves. These tips easily puncture the skin, a common painful occurrence for persons walking among them.

Blooms January–June.

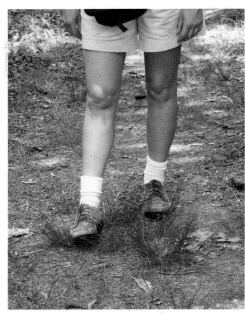

Helen Hamilton

Path Rush

Juncus tenuis   JUNCACEAE Rush Family

Description. This is a short perennial about 1 foot tall, with flat or inrolled leaves around the base that ascend or curve gently away from the stems. A cluster of flowers, which are wind-pollinated, appears at the end of the stem. The seed capsule of each flower splits into 3 sections, releasing minute dust-like seeds.

Habitat. Path Rush withstands trampling and is often found in and along footpaths, in heavy clay-loam, clay, or gravelly soil. While preferring sun or light shade and wet soils, this rush tolerates a considerable dry period. Growing in every county in Virginia, the plant is widespread throughout North America, and has spread to other continents, including Eurasia and Australia.

Comments. The species name *tenuis* means "slender." This weedy species prefers disturbed habitats, growing well in compacted soil. Because the tiny seeds become sticky when wet, they cling readily to the feathers of birds, fur of mammals, shoes of humans, and tires of motor vehicles, hence Path Rush is often seen along footpaths and roadways.

Blooms June–September.

256

Bulbous Woodrush

NATIVE

Luzula bulbosa   JUNCACEAE Rush Family

Description. This small perennial has grass-like leaves only ¼ inch wide with hairy margins, characteristic of woodrushes. Small white bulblets, representing reduced storage leaves, are at the base of the plant. The flowers are tiny, the 6 tepals with shiny chestnut centers in dense cylindric clusters at the tips of long branches of the inflorescence. The fruit is a 3-seeded capsule. Three similar species range across the Coastal Plain. There are only 1 to 4 flowers in each cluster of Hairy Woodrush *(L. acuminata)*. Some branches of the inflorescence of Spreading Woodrush *(L. echinata)* are wide-spreading, and the flower clusters globose to conical. The inflorescence branches of Common Woodrush *(L. multiflora)* are nearly erect as in Bulbous Woodrush, but the flower clusters are shorter, the perianth is dull, and basal bulblets are absent.

Habitat. Bulbous Woodrush is widespread across Virginia in dry forests, thickets, and clearings. It ranges from Florida to Texas north to Massachusetts, Pennsylvania, and Kansas.

Comments. *Luzula* may derive from Latin *lux*, meaning "light," because of dewdrops shining on parts of the plant. A tiny nutritive body on the seeds of some species facilitates dispersal by ants.

Blooms March–August.

Helen Hamilton

Woolgrass

NATIVE

Scirpus cyperinus   CYPERACEAE Sedge Family

Description. Although it is not a grass, its common name describes the fuzzy red-brown flower heads, large and drooping, very prominent along roadsides in autumn. At maturity numerous soft bristles emerge from the clustered spikelets, presenting a woolly appearance. This perennial sedge grows to 6 feet tall, usually in large clumps, and often in extensive colonies. The leaves are long and conspicuous, especially the basal ones. The fruit of grasses is a one-seeded grain, while that of rushes is a many-seeded capsule. The fruit of Woolgrass is a one-seeded achene. Woolgrass goes dormant in winter but adds a good deal of interest with the standing foliage.

Habitat. Common in roadside ditches, marshes, swamps, and wet meadows, this sedge is native to most counties of Virginia and ranges from Newfoundland to British Columbia and south to Florida and Texas.

Comments. *Scirpus* is the Latin name of bulrushes, now classified in several genera. Woolgrass can provide erosion control beside streams and ponds. The Ojibwa made mats and storage bags from the stems of this plant and used the fruiting tops for stuffing and making pillows. Bulrushes in general provide food and cover for wildlife—seeds for waterfowl and edible roots for geese and muskrats.

Blooms July–September.

Glossary

achene a small, dry one-seeded fruit with a thin wall

annual plant that germinates, blooms, produces and disperses seeds, and dies in a year

anther a pouch with pollen at the end of a slender stalk (filament) in the male part of a flower

awn a slender bristle-like appendage

axil the angle between a leaf or branch and the stem above it

axis the main stem of a plant about which plant parts such as leaves and branches are arranged

biennial plants that develop leaves, stems and roots the first year, bloom, fruit and die the second year

blade the broad part of a leaf, as distinguished from the stalk or petiole

bract a small leaflike or scalelike plant part usually located just below a flower

bracteole a small bract

calcareous soils formed from the weathering of limestone or fossil shell beds

calyx all the sepals of a flower, collectively

corolla all the petals of a flower

corona An extra outgrowth of tissue in some flowers in the form of a fringe, cup or tube, as the tube of daffodils

culm the stem of a plant, especially of a grass or sedge

endemic a species restricted to a specific region or habitat

ephemeral a plant that grows for a short time only, as the spring wildflowers

exserted projecting beyond the surrounding parts

floret an individual flower of a definite cluster, as in the head of an aster or the spikelet of a grass

glabrous smooth, without hairs or soft down

glaucous a whitish or bluish cast on leaves, stems, or fruits from a fine, waxy covering on the surface

inflorescence a cluster of flowers on a branch or stem

lemma in grasses, the lower bract enclosing the flower

ligule a projection at the base of the leaf blade in the grasses

259

loment a dry fruit with constrictions between the seeds, breaking into one-seeded segments when mature *(Desmodium)*

node the part of the stem where the leaves or branches attach

ovary swollen portion of a pistil, containing ovules, which become seeds inside a fruit

ovate, ovoid shaped like a long-section through a hen's egg, with the larger end toward the base

palmate resembling a hand with fingers spread

panicle a cluster of flowering branches, the individual branches being racemes

pedicel the stalk attaching a single flower to the main stem

peduncle the stalk supporting a flower cluster

perianth the outer part of a flower; the petals and sepals

perennial a plant that lives longer than two years

petiole the stalk of a leaf

pilose covered with long, soft straight hairs

pinnate feather-like, with veins or leaflets on each side of a central axis

pistil the female element of a flower, usually consisting of stigmas, styles, and ovary

pistillate having pistils or having female flowers

pubescent covered with soft down or short hairs

raceme an elongated flower cluster with the individual flowers stalked

rachis the main axis of a structure with multiple components, such as an inflorescence or a compound leaf

reflexed bent backward or downward

rhizome a horizontal, underground stem

sepal the part of the flower that covers the petals when in bud, usually green

sessile attached directly to the stem, without a petiole or flower stalk

spadix a spike with small flowers crowded on a thick stem

spathe a large bract enclosing a flower cluster, such as a spadix

spike an elongate flower cluster with the individual flowers without stalks (sessile)

spikelet a small or secondary spike; the flower cluster of grasses and sedges, consisting of one to many flowers with bracts

stamen the male element of a flower, usually composed of a stalk called the filament and an anther containing pollen sacs

staminate having stamens or having male flowers

stigma in the female part of a flower, the sticky surface where the pollen becomes attached

stipule one of a pair of leaflike appendages at the base of the petiole in some leaves

stolon an elongate horizontal stem that roots at the nodes or at the tip, forming new plants

style in the female part of a flower, the stalk holding the stigma where the pollen germinates

tepals the individual parts of the perianth, i.e., the sepals and petals, especially when very similar to one another, as in lilies

transverse at right angles

References

Coffey, T. 1993. *The History and Folklore of North American Wildflowers.* Houghton Mifflin Company, Boston.

Diggs, G.M., Jr., B.L. Lipscomb, and R.J. O'Kennon. 1999. *Shinners & Mahler's Illustrated Flora of North Central Texas.* Botanical Research Institute of Texas, Fort Worth.

Diggs, G.M., Jr., B.L. Lipscomb, M.D. Reed, and R.J. O'Kennon. 2006. *Illustrated Flora of East Texas, Volume One: Introduction, Pteridophytes, Gymnosperms, and Monocotyledons.* Botanical Research Institute of Texas, Fort Worth.

Digital Atlas of the Virginia Flora. 2013. Available online. http://vaplantatlas.org/

Duncan, W.H., and M.B. Duncan. 1987. *Seaside Plants of the Gulf and Atlantic Coasts.* Smithsonian Institution Press, Washington.

Fernald, M.L. 1950. *Gray's Manual of Botany,* 8th ed. American Book Company, New York.

Foster, S., and J.A. Duke. 1990. *Eastern/Central Medicinal Plants.* Peterson Field Guides, Houghton Mifflin Company, Boston.

Gleason, H.A., and A. Cronquist. 1991. *Manual of Vascular Plants of Northeastern United States and Adjacent Canada,* 2nd ed. The New York Botanical Garden, Bronx.

Gupton, O.W., and F.C. Swope. 1982. *Wildflowers of Tidewater Virginia.* University Press of Virginia, Charlottesville.

Holmgren, N.H. 1998. *Illustrated Companion to Gleason and Cronquist's Manual.* The New York Botanical Garden, Bronx.

Newcomb, L. 1977. *Newcomb's Wildflower Guide.* Little, Brown and Co., New York.

Niering, W.A. 1995. *National Audubon Society Field Guide to North American Wildflowers.* Alfred A. Knopf, New York.

Peterson, L.A. 1977. *A Field Guide to Edible Wild Plants.* Houghton Mifflin Company, Boston.

Peterson, R.T. 1996. *A Field Guide to Wildflowers, Northeastern and North-central North America.* Houghton Mifflin Company, Boston.

Radford, A.E., H.E. Ahles, and C.R. Bell. 1967. *Manual of the Vascular Flora of the Carolinas.* The University of North Carolina Press, Chapel Hill.

Silberhorn, G.M. 1999. *Common Plants of the Mid-Atlantic Coast: A Field Guide.* The Johns Hopkins University Press, Baltimore.

Stuckey, I.H., and L.L. Gould. 2000. *Coastal Plants from Cape Cod to Cape Canaveral.* The University of North Carolina Press, Chapel Hill.

Tiner, R.W. 1993. *Field Guide to Coastal Wetland Plants of the Southeastern United States.* The University of Massachusetts Press, Amherst.

United States Department of Agriculture Plants Database. Available online. http://www.plants.usda.gov

Venning, F.D. 1984. *Wildflowers of North America.* Golden Press, New York.

Virginia Department of Conservation and Recreation. September 2003. *Invasive Exotic Plant Species of Virginia.* Division of Natural Heritage, Richmond, Virginia.

Weakley, A.S., J.C. Ludwig, and J. F. Townsend. 2012. *Flora of Virginia.* B. Crowder, ed. Foundation of the Flora of Virginia Project Inc., Richmond. Botanical Research Institute of Texas Press, Fort Worth.

Further Reading

Brown, L. 1979. *Grasses: An Identification Guide.* Houghton Mifflin Company, New York.

Burrell, C.C. 2006. *Native Alternatives to Invasive Plants.* Brooklyn Botanic Garden, Inc. Brooklyn, New York.

Clark, L.G., and R.W. Pohl. 1996. *Agnes Chase's First Book of Grasses.* Smithsonian Institution Press, Washington, DC.

Densmore, F. 1974. *How Indians Use Wild Plants for Food, Medicine and Crafts.* Dover Publications Inc. New York.

Dunne, N. (ed.). 2009. *Great Natives for Tough Places.* Brooklyn Botanic Garden Inc., Brooklyn.

Erichsen-Brown, C. 1979. *Medicinal and Other Uses of North American Plants.* Dover Publications Inc., New York.

Fleming, C., M.B. Lobstein, and B. Tufty. 1995. *Finding Wildflowers in the Washington-Baltimore Area.* The Johns Hopkins University Press, Baltimore.

Grissell, E. 2001. *Insects and Gardens: In Pursuit of a Garden Ecology.* Timber Press, Portland, Oregon.

Holmes, R. (ed.). 1997. *Taylor's Guide to Ornamental Grasses.* Houghton Mifflin Company, New York.

Loewer, P. 2003. *Ornamental Grasses for the Southeast.* Cool Springs Press, Nashville, Tennessee.

Loewer, P. 2004. *Native Perennials for the Southeast.* Cool Springs Press, Nashville, Tennessee.

Mader, E., M. Shepherd, M. Vaughn, S. Black, and G. LeBuhn. 2011. *Attracting Native Pollinators.* The Xerces Society Guide, Storey Publishing, North Adams, Massachussetts.

Martin, L.C. 1993. *Wildflower Folklore.* The Globe Pequot Press, Old Saybrook, Connecticut.

Midgley, J.W. 1999. *Southeastern Wildflowers.* Crane Hill Publishers, Birmingham, Alabama.

Stein, S. 1993. *Noah's Garden: Restoring the Ecology of Our Own Back Yards.* Houghton Mifflin Company, New York.

Tallamy, D.W. 2007. *Bringing Nature Home: How You Can Sustain Wildlife with Native Plants.* Timber Press, Portland, Oregon.

Wasowski, S., and A. Wasowski. 1994. *Gardening with Native Plants of the South.* Taylor Trade Publishing, Lanham, Maryland.

Index to Scientific and Common Names

267

271

273